PUBLIC HEALTH PAPERS

No. 14

DEPRIVATION OF MATERNAL CARE

A Reassessment of its Effects

DEPRIVATION
OF MATERNAL CARE

A Reassessment of its Effects

CONTRIBUTORS

Mary D. Ainsworth — R. G. Andry
Robert G. Harlow — S. Lebovici — Margaret Mead
Dane G. Prugh — Barbara Wootton

WORLD HEALTH ORGANIZATION

GENEVA
1962

PRINTED IN SWITZERLAND

CONTENTS

PREFACE

Bowlby's monograph Maternal Care and Mental Health *was published by the World Health Organization in 1951,*[1] *and was at once acclaimed as an unequalled contribution to its subject. Its success is shown by the frequency with which it has been printed and the many languages into which it has been translated.*

The conclusion Bowlby reaches in his monograph is that the prolonged deprivation of the young child of maternal care may have grave and far-reaching effects on his character and so on the whole of his future life ; and he draws the corollary that the proper care of children deprived of a normal home life is not merely an act of common humanity, but essential to the mental and social welfare of a community. His indictment on that score of the nurseries, institutions, and hospitals of even the so-called advanced countries has contributed to a remarkable change in outlook that has led to a widespread improvement in the institutional care of children.

While the practical effects of Bowlby's monograph in the realm of child care have been universally acknowledged to be wholly beneficial, his theoretical conclusions have been subjected to a considerable amount of criticism. Some of this criticism is scarcely to the point, for it taxes Bowlby with failing to take into account aspects of deprivation that he himself deliberately omitted, either because he had not space within the limits of a monograph to deal with them or because he did not consider that there was sufficient evidence to pronounce upon them. Some of the criticism is based on misinterpretations of his views, which have been widely publicized in often over-simplified, extreme, or distorted forms. Other criticism, however, disputes the conclusions he has drawn from the evidence, or the value of the evidence itself. Finally, in the ten years that have elapsed since his monograph was published, there has inevitably been further research into the problem of maternal deprivation, and the problem has come to be viewed in a wider perspective—Bowlby has himself incorporated ethological theories into his views of child development.

---

[1] Bowlby, J. (1951) *Maternal care and mental health,* Geneva (*World Health Organization Monograph Series,* No. 2); 2nd edition, 1952.

Since there is a certain amount of confusion about the present position of Bowlby's theory about maternal deprivation, the time was considered ripe to attempt a reassessment in the light of advances in the last ten years and criticisms of the theory. A number of distinguished workers in child psychiatry and in allied fields were invited to discuss some of the issued involved. To these authors the World Health Organization owes a debt of gratitude for their contributions.

Because of pressing commitments, Dr Bowlby was unable himself to contribute a paper giving his present views, but this gap has been ably filled by his colleague Dr Ainsworth, with whose paper Dr Bowlby is in full agreement. There can be little doubt that the balanced view Dr Ainsworth takes of the evidence and the cautious conclusions she reaches not only take the issue out of the area of controversy but also present the research worker with a series of fascinating questions whose solution in the future would go far towards settling the problem of maternal deprivation.

For it cannot be said that this publication is the last word on the problem of deprivation. Bowlby's original study was limited to countries of Western Europe and North America, and he was unable to incorporate into it experience of deprivation in Eastern European countries—where the changes in the social role of women have been even more pronounced than in the West. Moreover, knowledge is lacking of deprivation in other countries of the world where the cultural situation and the status of women are totally different. Nor have such factors as paternal deprivation and its interaction with maternal deprivation been fully explored, or the analysis of deprivation itself been carried as far as it could conceivably be. This reassessment does not claim, therefore, to offer a definitive solution to the problem of deprivation. But it is hoped that it will at least provide a stimulus to further research into a problem that is of the greatest importance not only for the care of children but also for the social life of the whole community.

"MASKED DEPRIVATION"
IN INFANTS AND YOUNG CHILDREN

DANE G. PRUGH* & ROBERT G. HARLOW**

It is the purpose of this chapter to give appropriate emphasis to certain factors in the mother-child relationship which are often crucial in determining the course of the child's personality development. More specifically, it is proposed to discuss the effects of various sorts of covert, subtle, or " masked " emotional deprivation which may result for the child in otherwise intact parent-child relationships, as opposed to those effects seen as a result of flagrant and gross physical separation of mother and child during the early years.

HISTORICAL REVIEW

Since the turn of the century, scientific awareness has existed regarding the possible adverse effects upon the emotional development of children institutionalized at an early age. Intuitive popular knowledge of these possibilities, however, has been available for a much longer period, as expressed, for example, in the works of such perceptive writers as Charlotte Brontë. [17] The paediatric literature was the first systematically to reflect this awareness, with the publication, in 1908, of Chapin's [21] observations on " atrophic " infants who had been in institutional settings for long periods of time. Later works in the fields of social welfare and education contributed significantly to knowledge in this area, as exemplified by the published studies of Theis [80] in 1924 and Aichhorn [1] in 1925. It was not until the late 1930's, however, that reports in the psychiatric and psychological literature began to appear. Such investigators as Powdermaker [61] and Levy, [47] followed by Lowrey, [54] Bowlby, [10] Bender, [5] Goldfarb, [36] and others, moved towards more careful description of the effects of early institutionalization, all being struck with the consequent disruption of

* Associate Professor of Psychiatry and Pediatrics, and Head, Child Psychiatry Division, University of Rochester School of Medicine and Dentistry and Strong Memorial Hospital, Rochester, N.Y., USA.

** Senior Clinical Instructor in Psychiatry (Psychology), and Supervising Psychologist, Child Psychiatry Division, University of Rochester School of Medicine and Dentistry and Strong Memorial Hospital, Rochester, N.Y., USA.

the capacity to form warm and lasting relationships on the part of children undergoing such experience. Goldfarb's work included controlled studies of the long-term effects of early institutional as opposed to foster-home care, indicating that the children reared in institutions were most disturbed. These and other investigations derived impetus from Sigmund Freud's earlier conclusions [32] regarding the important influence of early experiences upon later personality development.

During the early 1940's, a number of significant studies were undertaken in this area. Burlingham & Freud [19] studied the frequently disturbing effects, as did Edelston,[27] of the separation of young children from their mothers, arising from the dislocations occasioned by the war events. The careful work of Spitz & Wolf [79] contributed more direct, systematic, and rigorous documentation of the sweeping and at times apparently irreversible psychological consequences of an unhealthy nature, arising from institutional placements with inadequate mother-substitute care during the first year of life. Blunting or serious distortion in intellectual, emotional, social, and physical aspects of growth and development appeared in such infants continuingly deprived, with serious depression appearing in others separated from their mothers during the latter part of the second half-year of life. During this period also, a number of workers, especially Bowlby [10] and Bender,[5] recognized the frequent later appearance of deep and pervasive character disorders with delinquent behavioural manifestations in children so severely deprived. The more recent observations of Roudinesco and her associates [72] and Fischer,[31] carried out upon young infants awaiting adoption, support the likelihood of the development of pathological reactions of a continuing nature.

From the field of paediatrics, Bakwin's observations,[3] extending earlier findings of Chapin [21] and Brenneman,[15] pointed up during this period the potentially detrimental effects of such virtually complete emotional deprivation upon physical as well as psychological development. He emphasized the possibility of the development of " marasmus ", a condition resembling starvation, as well as heightened morbidity and mortality from infectious disease, in young infants hospitalized for long periods of time. His work, like that of Beverly,[9] thus dealt with infants and young children with chronic physical disease, in contrast to the physically healthy children, institutionalized because of lack of home facilities, who were studied by the other investigators mentioned. Similar effects upon physical development were observed, however, in such healthy institutionalized infants, as reported by Spitz & Wolf,[79] echoing earlier reports in the European literature.[4]

In addition to these observations upon the results of gross and prolonged or repeated deprivation of maternal care in institutional or hospital settings, more recent work has been carried out in regard to the impact of briefer separation from the mother, principally involved in hospitalization for physical illness or operation. Among others, Levy,[49] Senn,[75] Langford,[46] J. C. Spence,* Jackson,[41] Bowlby and associates,[12] Jessner, Blom & Waldfogel,[43] Moncrieff,[57] Faust and co-workers,[30] Wallace & Feinauer,[81] Prugh and his associates,[65] Schaffer,[73] and Robertson,[70, 71] have added to our knowledge of the effects of experiences of this nature for infants and young children, drawing upon points of view and methods of study derived from the fields of psychiatry, psychology, social work, paediatrics, and nursing. In general, studies in this area have indicated the universality of significant reactions of a depressive, regressive, or anxiety-provoking nature in children undergoing such experience. In most instances these reactions to brief separation in a medical setting appear to be short-lived. Children under four years of age and previously disturbed older children with unsatisfying parent-child relationships, however, may suffer more lasting interference with emotional development.

EVALUATION OF BOWLBY'S WORK

Of the studies mentioned, the most influential, perhaps, has been that of Bowlby. His monograph, *Maternal Care and Mental Health*,[11] contained an exhaustive review of world literature up to that time, as well as reports of his own studies and certain conclusions drawn from all these sources. The evidence marshalled by Bowlby appeared impressively in support of the likelihood of serious personality disturbance, manifested by shallow relationships, difficulties in impulse control, and at times limitations in cognitive and perceptual functions, arising from prolonged institutionalization or frequent foster-home placement in early childhood. Bowlby states,

" Prolonged breaks [in the mother-child relationship] during the first three years of life leave a characteristic impression on the child's personality. Clinically such children appear emotionally withdrawn and isolated. They fail to develop libidinal ties with other children or with adults and consequently have no friendships worth the name " (p. 32). [11]

He sums up his conclusions by advancing the hypothesis that "there is a specific connexion between prolonged deprivation in the early years and the development of an affectionless psychopathic character given to persistent delinquent conduct and extremely difficult to treat " (p. 34).[11]

---

* " The care of children in hospitals " (The Charles West Lecture, Royal College of Physicians, London, November 1946).

The importance of Bowlby's contributions is unquestioned. As a result of his report, the dangers of gross maternal deprivation have become clear to workers in many professional fields and in all parts of the world. Significant efforts have been initiated in certain quarters and renewed in others in order to do away with the conditions leading to such results. Unfortunately, however, some of the implications of Bowlby's statements in his monograph have been accepted so completely and uncritically by certain professional workers that emphasis has been diverted at times from questions which remain unanswered and from other considerations which deserve equal attention.

Although Bowlby himself recognized that such was not the case, the interpretation has been made from his work that any separation of the infant or young child from the mother necessarily results in serious emotional deprivation. Some of the investigations cited earlier, dealing with reactions to brief hospitalization, refute sweeping mis-statements of this kind and indicate that multiple factors play a role in the development of pathological reactions to experience of this nature.

The additional conclusion has been drawn, by many professional workers, that all children undergoing early institutionalization or other sorts of gross maternal deprivation develop the picture of the " affectionless character ", sketched by Bowlby, on the basis of his own work and the other studies cited earlier. Furthermore, the inference has been loosely made by some that only children experiencing this type of extreme deprivation will exhibit this particular personality picture.

Reports are meagre in this area and control or comparison studies are difficult to undertake on a long-term basis. The careful investigation of Heinecke,[40] involving a controlled study of very young children in residential and day nurseries, appears to support the position that separation does leave a demonstrable effect on the child's immediate adjustment, but this study does not deal with the long-term consequences of such experiences. The earlier work of Dennis,[23] the recent critique of Bowlby's work by O'Connor,[58] and the studies of changes in intellectual functioning over time by Clarke & Clarke [22] would seem, however, to cast some doubt upon both the universality and the enduring nature of such personality pictures in relation to early experience of the type described. Moreover, the work of Theis [80] and of Beres & Obers,[7] cited by Bowlby, and the investigations of Lewis,[50] Goldfarb,[37] and Fischer,[31] suggest that some children may escape such deep personality scars, again appearing to confirm intuitive perceptions of creative writers such as Dickens [25] and others.

Although the answer to this question remains to be clarified more fully, the later work of Bowlby, Ainsworth, Boston & Rosenbluth [14] provides some pertinent data. In a study which has not yet received as full attention as Bowlby's earlier monograph, they investigated systematically the long-term effects of separation from the mother, over periods of months or years before the fourth birthday, in a group of children who had been patients in a tuberculosis sanatorium. Using a group of healthy children as controls, they found that, although the sanatorium children were significantly less well adjusted than the controls, the differences between the two groups were not as great as had been expected in terms of their hypothesis. In addition, they found that few of the sanatorium children appeared to be delinquent and that at least half of them were able to make some satisfying social relationships. Although the maternal deprivation suffered by these children was not as intense as in Goldfarb's study, Bowlby and his co-workers came, on the basis of these findings, to the conclusion that, " Statements implying that children who experience institutionalization and similar forms of severe privation in early life *commonly* develop psychopathic or affectionless characters are incorrect ". The further conclusion was made that the retrospective follow-up method of investigation contained inherent disadvantages which limited its use in this area of research.

The reasons for this seeming " immunity " from marked psychological disorders in some children undergoing experience of this nature are not clearly understood. Factors relating to genetic endowment may be involved, as well as special environmental circumstances—e.g., the child's attractiveness or personal appeal to one or more institutional workers may lead them to give the child special care or attention. Nevertheless, sweeping conclusions regarding the outcome of such experience do not appear to be justified, although, as Bowlby and his co-workers indicated, their later study offered no grounds for complacency as to the effects of gross maternal deprivation.

In regard to the related question whether " affectionless characters " develop only as a result of gross maternal deprivation, clinical observations at least would lend ample support to the thesis that such is not the case. The work of Aichhorn,[1] Lippman,[51] and others (including the present writers) provides a number of case examples of children exhibiting such characterological patterns and experiencing chronic difficulty with the authorities, with the parents always available to plead the child's case for him, in spite of their ambivalent or hostile feelings towards him in other respects. In summary, then, it would seem that early institutionalization or prolonged separation from parents does not *necessarily* lead to specific effects upon personality in later life, and that these personality patterns, when they are observed, are not *always* due to a particular set of early experiences.

A further conclusion that has sometimes been drawn is that any home setting is better than any institutional placement. Case studies by Du Pan & Roth [26] and by many other workers, including the present writers, attest to the fact that the physical presence of a parent or a foster-parent does not guarantee emotional satisfaction to the child, especially if that parent is unable to tolerate any disturbance in behaviour on the part of the child. If a foster-home setting is involved, a train of events leading to repetitive shifts in home settings, with serious emotional consequences for the child, may be set in motion in the absence of careful selection of foster-parents and of much work by the placement agency.

Finally, misplaced emphasis given to Bowlby's earlier statements can lead to the facile conclusion that any child at any age is better off in his own home than in a foster-home, hospital, or other institutional setting. It is true that most children are happier with their own parents, no matter how disturbed or unsatisfying the parent-child relationships may be. However, recent experiences in nurseries and residential treatment centres, which have admitted disturbed children from physically intact but seriously disturbed families, have indicated that the home may not always be the most favourable environment for a child's development. On the contrary, it is sometimes seen that only when the child is removed from the home is he able to begin to mature and develop.

" MASKED DEPRIVATION "

Although Bowlby recognized the existence of what he called " partial deprivation " in children involved in an unsatisfying relationship with the mother, he purposely chose not to include studies of this nature in his monograph, rather emphasizing the " complete deprivation " in cases of the type mentioned. (He also designedly excluded father-child relationships from scrutiny, again for purposes of emphasis.) It is the position of the writers, in agreement with the views of Bakwin [4] and Glaser & Eisenberg,[35] that the subtle effects of less obvious disruptions or distortions in the parent-child relationship may have as devastating effects upon emotional development as the more gross maternal deprivations highlighted by Bowlby. Further, it is to be emphasized that instances of " masked " or covert deprivation, of a virtually "complete" nature, may occur frequently in intact families, giving rise to clinical pictures in children which may equal in pathological intensity those derived from overt deprivations. Spitz's studies [78] of the so-called psychogenic disorders of infancy support this conclusion in regard to the influence of what he termed a " deficiency " of maternal warmth and affection upon emotional development in infancy and early childhood and the associated appearance of certain psychophysiological disorders. The more recent observations by Provence & Coleman [62] indicate that the syndrome of " environmental retardation ", described earlier by Gesell & Amatruda [34] can occur in infants living in intact homes. This syndrome, aptly described by Clarke & Clarke, [22] appears to involve the particular effects of insufficient maternal warmth and stimulation upon the intellectual development of certain infants, producing a picture resembling mental retardation without associated brain damage or other cause. With the provision of satisfying mother-substitute relationships or with the use of direct psychotherapeutic work with the mother, such retardation appears to be reversible. This more subtle, but apparently equally potent, psychological " separation " or deprivation seems to deserve re-emphasis at this time and to require more careful description and dynamic formulation.

CLINICAL OBSERVATIONS

We shall now consider some clinical examples from our own experience of parent-child relationships which involve no actual or physical separation but which may be said to involve emotional separation or deprivation. What follows is not meant to be an exhaustive analysis, nor is it intended to imply that the emotional deprivation is necessarily the sole factor determining the symptom picture observed. In this regard, the case histories have been purposely condensed and simplified, and factors not directly relevant to the point at issue have been omitted. A few clinical illustrations will be presented, however, which suggest the marked effect of intense but subtle and covert deprivation upon personality development. The common factor in all these instances is the physical intactness of the family unit.

In the presentation of such clinical material, no effort will be made to erect an elaborate classification of parent-child relationships. No such satisfactory classification as yet exists, and a variety of descriptive terms have been employed. The available terminology is somewhat loose and overlapping, dealing variably with the affect experienced by the parent towards the child, such as hostility, or with the behavioural aspects of the parent-child interaction, as in over-protective or rejecting situations. In dealing phenomenologically with the problem of the adequacy of emotional supplies given to the infant by the mother, the nature and degree of relatedness will be considered. At least two major ways of perceiving and relating to the child appear to exist. The first involves the situation in which the child has a specific but distorted meaning for the parent; hence a relationship develops in which the child is not viewed as an individual with integrity in his own right, but rather, in some way, as a being responding to the needs, wishes, and feelings of the parent, with the result that his emotional needs are not met adequately. This situation will be termed " distorted relatedness. " The second way in which the child may be perceived by his parents, leading to pathological development, is one in which the child does not have any such specific meaning to the parent; the parent, however, is so involved in his own concerns, whether of a transient or of an enduring nature, that he is unable to provide adequate emotional supplies or, more broadly, adequate parenting for the infant. This situation we shall call " insufficient relatedness. " We shall attempt to provide, subsumed under each of these categories, examples of different sorts of reaction in the parent — i.e., the varying affects experienced by the parent figures, the different ways in which these affects are expressed, and what seems to be the answering response in the behaviour patterns of the children.

Distorted relatedness

(1) The mother (or father) may be unable to perceive the child as an individual separate from herself (or himself) and may handle the child accordingly, with little or no regard for the child's own needs.

(a) In extreme examples the parent may be completely confused as to the identity of the child and the child essentially undifferentiated from the parent.

Example: A chronically psychotic woman, living at home with her husband, gave birth to a female infant who she said was the incarnation of her mother. She had previously been confused as to whether she was herself or her mother. This confusion was revived and, instead of feeding her infant, she often lay down beside the infant, opening her mouth and saying, " Feed me ". In spite of the urgings of her husband, an ineffectual person, she was unable to feed the infant more than occasionally but refused frequently to permit her husband to feed her. Although the husband managed to give the infant some surreptitious feedings, her nutritional state became precarious over the course of several months. The mother could not accept either medical care for the infant or psychiatric hospitalization for herself. Finally the neighbours, seeing the infant's marasmic state, forced the husband to steal the baby away from the mother and take her to a hospital.

(b) Less extreme, but still deeply pathological, examples involve situations in which a relationship is established wherein either the parents' or the child's needs can only be gratified through the other's response. Hence each is dependent upon the other's actions for his or her own satisfactions. This represents the so-called symbiotic or complementary relationship.

Example: A markedly obese girl had been constantly fed large amounts of food by the mother, who had adopted her in early infancy. Here the mother's need to offer this child nutritional supplies appeared to operate in part as a substitute for her incapacity to provide emotional supplies of a satisfying nature, because of her own conflicts in the role of woman and mother. Her associated need to keep the girl, whom she called " Baby ", in a state of infantile dependence upon her appeared to derive in part from her unsatisfying and unsuccessful marital relationship with an immature, alcoholic husband. At a deeper level, she regarded the girl as a part of herself which needed gratification, but was also dependent upon the girl's clinging response to her. In spite of the mother's constant feeding, over-protective and controlling behaviour towards the girl, she readily permitted her to be placed in a convalescent hospital for nearly a year, and her underlying hostility towards the girl showed in her reluctance to have her return to the home. The girl at the age of 12 presents the picture of a firmly entrenched passive-aggressive personality disorder, with markedly unsatisfied emotional needs and the tendency to over-eat as a substitute for healthier gratifications.

(2) In other instances, while the child may be perceived as a separate person, the parent may still respond in terms of his or her own needs.

(a) In some instances, the significant parent may identify the child with certain aspects of himself or of other persons; the interaction with the child may then take place in terms of these projected personality attributes or partial identifications.

Example: A mother had experienced deep anger at her own father for his coolness towards her. She permitted her infant daughter's rebellion towards her husband, identifying the daughter with herself and her husband with her father. When the little girl stole objects from her father, the mother laughed and thought her behaviour " cute ", while superficially criticizing her. She could only relate warmly to the girl when she acted out towards her husband, at other times pushing her off, saying she was " too busy " to talk to her. The girl became delinquent, stealing from boys and becoming involved sexually with a series of men, without any real gratification in such relationships.

Example: An essentially normally endowed boy was brought up by a mother whose social aspirations kept her constantly preoccupied, although physically present in the home. The early care of the child was completely in the hands of a succession of maids and governesses, none of whom remained for more than a few months because of the mother's critical attitude towards them. The father, a large and athletic man who had achieved business success by his driving ambition, tried to pattern his son upon his own ideals, forcing him to perform rigorous and exhausting exercises daily and to read widely in esoteric fields in order to gain a fund of knowledge which would equip him for any emergency. Beginning with the pre-school period, the boy became exceedingly anxious and inhibited, with strong phobic trends and a marked stammer, thus accentuating his failure to achieve the father's unrealistic goals and losing the one dimension of contact and interest with his father, the only parent who had any real involvement with him.

Example: A woman gave birth to a male infant who greatly resembled her husband, with whom she had a close relationship. He died when the boy was six months of age, and the mother spent most of her time for the next several years dressing the boy to " look like his father ". It was clear that she had not worked through her depressed feelings over her husband's death, partly because her own father had died when she was a young girl. She could not relate to the boy except through her identification of him with her husband, and even then without adequate warmth, and he became rebellious towards her handling of him, constantly running away and eventually becoming involved with a group of delinquent boys.

Example: A woman gave birth to her first child, a boy, in a setting of considerable marital conflict. She had made a neurotic choice in her marriage and could neither accept nor leave her husband, being bound to him in a hostile-dependent relationship. From the first she seemingly projected the hostility she felt towards the father on to this infant. She said that she could not accept him and paid him little attention except during feeding. When he refused food, she became openly angry and would take his plate away, expressing openly her dislike of him. The child ate very poorly, developing a picture of extreme undernourishment, with the result that he weighed only 19 lb. at 4½ years and was the size of a two-year-old. Gradually his state of nutrition and hydration became precarious, necessitating medical treatment. With psychiatric help, the mother was finally able to place him in another setting, whereupon he gained 15 lb. within a few weeks.

(*b*) Parents may, in addition, possess irrational and distorted perceptions of their children, arising not from identification but from basic attitudes, acquired values and standards, or other aspects of their previous experience.

Example: A male infant was born with a mis-shapen head and experienced significant brain damage during the birth process. The mother, a woman with intense needs for perfection in the mother role, felt deeply ambivalent towards this boy from the first, finding herself unable to look at him without feeling that she had failed as a woman in producing a damaged child. In order to compensate for her feelings of disgust and guilt in her relationship to this boy, she had appeared to repress and deny such anxiety-provoking affects, attempting to handle him as a completely normal child. Her intense stimulation of this boy beyond his limited capacities and her over-protective and strongly controlling behaviour towards him resulted in adequate physical care, but a serious lack of warmth and affection between them. Over the first three years of life, the boy developed an extremely withdrawn state, isolating himself from the mother and failing to respond to her stimulations, thus increasing her unconscious hostility towards him and diminishing even further the limited emotional supplies which she could give to him.

Example: A boy was regarded from infancy as mentally retarded by the mother because of his initial lack of responsiveness to her. Although she hovered constantly around him in a protective fashion, she remained emotionally isolated and withdrawn from him and looked on him as a family disgrace. The boy in turn became increasingly withdrawn, with shallow relationships. Gradually he conformed to the mother's perception of him as retarded, by his complete lack of scholastic achievement despite high average to superior intellectual endowment.

Insufficient relatedness

(1) The parent may, because of unhealthy characterological or deeply neurotic or psychotic trends, quite independent of the child, be unable to relate warmly to the infant.

(*a*) The mother may be a cold and isolated personality, with little or no ability to " give " emotionally to her child.

Example: A mother, an attractive but seriously inhibited and cold young woman, felt completely unable to respond to her first-born infant, a boy. She went through the motions of his care, but was consciously aware that she felt no warmth towards him and took no pleasure in him at any time. Although she remained close to him physically, she let him play alone for many hours in his playpen during the first year of life, withdrawing into herself or reading and paying only occasional attention to his safety. During the latter part of the boy's second year, the father became alarmed at the child's lack of responsiveness or interest in the environment, and upon psychiatric study an autistic psychotic picture was apparent.

(*b*) The parents may be so involved in their own narcissistic needs or pleasures that any emotional warmth for the child is precluded, even though physical care is provided.

Example: In a particular family, the father was an expert bowler, who spent all his spare time in this activity. As a result of his need to prove himself in competition, he took no interest in his eldest son, even when the boy grew old enough to imitate his father, leaving his care completely to the mother. The mother was a helpless and dependent person, who was frightened of the boy's healthy aggression as an infant and of his growing masculinity. She could set no limits on his aggressive behaviour, " washing her hands " of him in early childhood, although she continued to care for his physical needs. The boy became an impulsive and antisocial personality, with inability to control his hostile and destructive impulses and with no adequate identification with a father figure.

(2) In other instances, situational factors involving current reality problems may produce psychological disorders in the parent which may affect detrimentally the developmental processes of the infant.

Example: A young mother experienced the death of her own mother during the latter part of her pregnancy with her second child. Although still able to minister to the physical needs of the infant, she felt that she had " nothing left to give " to him. During the first eight months of the infant's life, the father was able to offer significant emotional support to the mother, although she remained definitely depressed, without a feeling of warmth for the infant. The father became ill suddenly, however, and temporarily lost his job, so that he also became depressed and apathetic and could no longer offer support to the mother. At this point, the infant developed marked diarrhoea of a non-infectious nature, showing an associated refusal of food, without underlying physical abnormalities. The combined loss of body fluids and the lack of nutritional intake produced a picture resembling that of marasmus. Strenuous medical therapy was of no avail, but the infant responded, with a cessation of diarrhoea and a resumption of feeding, to the assignment in the hospital of one warm and " giving " nurse to his principal care. Supportive psychotherapy for the parents enabled the mother to lose her depression and the father to conquer his apathy and secure a job. Upon returning home under these circumstances, the infant resumed normal development with no subsequent difficulties over a number of years.

DISCUSSION

It is recognized that multiple etiological forces are at work in the cases cited and that " masked deprivation " may not represent the sole cause of the symptom pictures observed. These examples, however, clearly suggest the markedly adverse effects of a faulty parent-child relationship, even under circumstances where the physical needs of the child are met. It is also evident that "masked deprivation" can be involved in the production of a variety of symptomatic pictures or personality disorders in the child, including examples of the so-called "affectionless character" described by Bowlby. No one symptom complex or personality pattern appears to predominate in persons whose early life was characterized by "masked deprivation". These conclusions, when taken in conjunction with the studies cited earlier, cast further doubt upon the specificity of the development of any personality configuration in response to any specific antecedent event.

It is proposed now to discuss some of the variables which may be important in determining the child's reaction to traumatic events during his early development. Because of the intensely unique quality of each parent-child dyad (occurring as it does in an interlocking network of marital and family interpersonal relationships at a particular point in time, and involving persons with idiosyncratic personality attributes), any event, whether it be actual separation, psychological estrangement from the parents, or some other significant happening, may have greatly varying effects on both parent and child.

During the past twenty-five years much attention has been devoted to the basic needs of the human infant. In addition to his physiological needs, equally essential for the infant is the receiving of affective warmth and stimulation from a maternal figure, as underscored by Ribble,[68] Spitz,[77] and others. Concepts such as "stimulus hunger" and "affect hunger", to use Levy's term,[47] suggest that the physical presence of a maternal figure alone is not sufficient to ensure for the infant the gratification of needs of this nature. The function of the mother in providing emotional supplies to the infant in its helpless state, and the answering "confidence" of the infant in her availability, have been emphasized.[6] Current conceptualizations also point up the importance to the mother of the infant's capacity to respond pleasurably to her ministrations. Some mothers have extreme difficulty in adjusting to a role in which they "give" but in which there tends to be little "return" for this giving — e.g., the infant who fails to smile responsively or who refuses to accept the breast or bottle. This maternal reaction to the child's lack of response, or "feedback", as Brody[16] and others have indicated, "feeds back" to the child, and a cycle of resentment and frustation in the mother-infant relationship tends to be established.

Variations in the capacity of the mother to satisfy the infant's affective needs may arise from her own neurotic problems, reflecting earlier unsolved conflicts, or from current difficulties in carrying out her maternal functions — e.g., disturbances in the marital relationship or in the balance of interpersonal forces within the family unit. On the infant's part, individual inborn or acquired differences in responsiveness may exist, as demonstrated by Bergmann & Escalona [8] and Fries,[33] thus affecting the quality of the " feedback " of satisfactions to the mother. The more recent writings of Bowlby [13] and others, drawing upon studies by ethologists such as Lorenz,[52] suggest the possibility also of innate patterns of response to the external environment, which in turn affect, and may be affected by, the mother's reaction to the behaviour of the infant or young child. Studies of the vicissitudes in the mother-infant relationship, as emphasized by Benedek,[6] Jacobsen [42] and others, as well as surveys of existing research by such workers as Orlansky,[59] suggest that the quality of these early reciprocal relationships, or the " emotional climate ", as Rank [67] has termed it, is more important for healthy emotional development than the effect of any single child-rearing technique.

In regard to separation, actual or psychological, it is already apparent that the effects of such experience upon the infant will vary according to its nature and length of duration, as well as to the quality of substitute maternal relationships available. (In some instances of " masked deprivation," arising particularly from insufficient relatedness between mother and infant, another female member of the family, or even occasionally the father, may provide adequate substitute relationships.)

An additional variable is represented by the age or stage of development of the infant or young child when separation or equivalent emotional trauma occurs. Most studies indicate that actual or symbolic separation from the mother during the first two or three months of life rarely disturbs the infant seriously if an adequate mother-substitute figure is provided. Separation after this time, when the infant has at hand the developmental capacities to begin to develop a definite object relationship with the mother, may be more disturbing, with disturbances appearing during the second quarter of the first year, as Fischer has indicated,[31] and involving " anaclitic depression ", described by Spitz & Wolf.[79] A particular point of vulnerability seems to be the period during the second half of the first year of life when the infant begins to be involved in differentiating himself from the mother and in developing a primitive body image, albeit in the context of an extremely dependent relationship. Some studies have suggested retardation of both physical and mental development, the impairment of the capacity to form close object relationships, and the failure to achieve ego differentiation, as a consequence of seriously impaired mother child relationships during this period.[22, 77] Separations taking place during the period from one to four years or so may still produce pathological effects, principally in regard to the capacity to form warm object relationships, and marked regression, difficulties in impulse control, and blunting or distortion of ego development can occur under deeply unhealthy circumstances.

Separations experienced after the first four years ordinarily seem to be less disturbing, since the child is less dependent, his reality testing is more adequate, and his capacities for object relationships are more solidly established. If markedly intense Oedipal conflicts are in process, however, difficulties in sexual identifications or other problems still may result.

As a parallel to human experience, many animal studies, including those by Seitz,[74] Allee,[2] and Harlow,[39] as well as experiments currently being conducted by R. Ader,* very strikingly indicate detrimental effects upon the organism's later functioning as a consequence of the controlled varying of its very early environment, whether this involves actual separation from the mother or various manipulations within the mother-infant relationship.

In addition to the development stage of the infant or young child at the time of occurrence of emotional trauma, the particular and unique conflicts with which the young child is dealing during that stage may influence his immediate response, the type of resulting symptomatology, and later personality development. Deutsch,[24] in particular, has stressed the effects, principally in terms of psychosomatic disorders, of the occurrence of a psychic trauma contiguous with the existence of significant conflicts at a time prior to the full development of the instinctive life. He feels, and cites numerous case examples, that in later life, when the " old " psychic conflict becomes active, specific and individually unique symptomatology develops. The same conceptual thinking is lucidly expressed by Eissler,[28] who considered the possibility that the child might be unable to reach higher developmental levels as a consequence of a marked trauma at a time when his early feelings of omnipotence constitued one of his main techniques for dealing with reality.

The prior nature of the mother-infant relationship would appear to represent an additional variable in the determination of the infant's response to separation or equivalent trauma. In this connexion, Spitz[79] has suggested that the infant who has, in general, a closer and more intensely satisfying relationship with his mother may suffer more from separation, actual or psychological, and may find a substitute more difficult to accept, at least immediately, than the infant who has received more limited gratification from his mother. The quality of the maternal relationship, or of its substitute following the separation, must also be recognized as an important factor.

A further variable which must be considered concerns the meaning of the child's trauma to the mother. Because of the extreme closeness of the parent-child unit, the mother's conflicts concerning and reaction

---

* At the University of Rochester Medical Center, Rochester, N.Y.

to events may determine, in part, particularly for the older infant and young child, the way in which the child accepts, deals with, and reacts to such things as separation, injuries, or the introduction of siblings into the family. Numerous cases in the literature and in the authors' experience, for example, suggest that the parent's reaction to the child's hospitalization for an operation is a factor of great importance in determining the response of the child to this situation, even though other variables are, of course, involved.

In summary, it would seem that the child's response to separation, as a representative potential trauma, is a complex process, influenced by its nature and duration, the quality of mothering before and after the experience, the age and stage of development of the child, and the emotional conflicts with which he is principally dealing. Also important are such factors as the child's physical health, his integrative or other ego capacities, the reaction of salient figures around him to the experience, and the nature of important later events. The influence of other variables such as the inborn or acquired biological capacities of the child are more difficult to assess but must also be considered.

In regard to distorted or insufficient relatedness between parent and child as one of the most important variables in this equation, the general literature provides many cases similar to those described in this chapter. Distorted relatedness would appear to predominate in the cases of " symbiotic psychosis " in childhood discussed by Mahler,[56] and in some of the examples of " atypical ego development " furnished by Rank and her co-workers.[66] In another symptomatic framework, certain of the parent-child relationships existing in cases of ulcerative colitis presented by Sperling [76] and Prugh [63] would appear to involve such distorted relatedness, as would some of the examples of clinging behaviour and obesity given by Levy [48] and Bruch.[18] Of particular relevance is the work with leukaemic patients by Greene,[38] who has described instances of the unconscious use of the child by the parent as a " vicarious object " in an attempt to adjust to separation from another significant person in the parent's life. In addition, Aichhorn [1] and Johnson [44] have given examples of apparently similar aberrations in parent-child relatedness, based on unconsciously distorted parental perceptions, in cases of delinquency.

In the area of insufficient relatedness, abundant examples can be cited from the infant studies of such workers as Richmond,[69] regarding rumination, Lourie,[53] in relation to malnutrition or vomiting, Prugh [64] and Prugh & Shwachman,* dealing with cases of coeliac disease and of diarrhoea

---

* Prugh, D. G. & Shwachman, H. " Observations on chronic unexplained diarrhea in infants and young children " (Paper given at a joint meeting of the British Paediatric Society, the Canadian Pediatric Society, and the Society for Pediatric Research, Quebec, Canada, June 1955).

of psychophysiological origin, and Spitz,[79] involving depression and marasmus. The case studied by Engel, Reichsman & Segal,[29] involving an infant with a gastric fistula, is particularly pertinent. The mother in this instance felt virtually unable to relate warmly to the child because of her conflicts over the abnormal feeding situation, and the infant developed depression associated with severe marasmus during the second half-year of life. The marasmus and depression responded to the provision of substitute-parent relationships in the hospital, with a later re-establishment of relatedness between mother and infant when the fistula had been repaired and a normal feeding situation made possible. Lourie [53] has described the treatment of similar cases in hospitals with such mother-substitute arrangements, together with psychotherapeutic help for the parents, particularly the mother. Finally, Kanner's studies [45] of " autistic " children reveal numerous examples of cold, detached mothers, unable, because of their own conflicts, to provide these particular children with emotional supplies from early infancy onwards.

Because of the complexity of the interaction among the multitude of variables which may vitally affect subsequent development, prediction of symptom formation even under conditions of very extreme emotional trauma would seem to possess, at present, a low level of confidence. While in a gross way we may foresee that some event will be likely to have a marked effect upon an individual personality, the complicated forces which determine the precise nature of this effect are still best seen in retrospect. Predictive studies in a life setting in which the salient events or variables are stated before the fact and are carefully controlled, in which there is an adequate measure of effects, and in which there are identical measurements of a comparable group which did not experience these events, are vitally needed. The investigations of Heinecke,[40] mentioned earlier, fulfil these conditions in large measure but do not involve long-term follow-up studies. Pease & Gardner [60] have recently set up such a predictive study on the effects of non-continuous mothering in early infancy. Follow-up data are as yet limited, however.

It seems important to emphasize that the state of our knowledge is such, at this time, that conclusions regarding the effects of early experience can be drawn only tentatively and then in quite general terms. No one symptom complex seems to eventuate consistently from one set of prior experiences, nor does any particular early event necessarily mark all those who experience it similarly. Significant trauma to the child may occur as a function of physical separation from the mother. This does not always occur, however, as the telling examples cited by Caplan [20] and J. Mann* of the *Kibbutzim* in Israel demonstrate, nor

---

* In a paper presented at the American Orthopsychiatric Meetings, 1957.

is this trauma always more severe in its effects than " psychological " separation with its consequent " masked deprivation ".

It would follow, then, that only with extreme care and close examination of the factors involved can one arrive at the best disposition of any given case. The conclusion, for example, that the child should continue to stay in its own home, or in a foster-home, under all conditions, does not seem warranted. Maenchen's statement is relevant here: " A child may never have been separated from his mother and yet have been deprived of much more than if he had been placed in an institution with small groups under good nurses ". [55] Under certain conditions of " masked deprivation ", then, proper institutional placement may therefore be the disposition of choice, if planned for wisely and with adequate preparation of the child and parents. A discussion of the types of institutional placement which can be arranged constructively is beyond the scope of this paper. The thoughtful review of Glaser & Eisenberg [35] deals with this topic, and the discussion by Du Pan & Roth [26] indicates methods of rendering the atmosphere in small institutions more emotionally healthy and satisfying for the children placed there.

It is important, then, to maintain a vigilant eye for the subtle and covert factors, as well as for the more gross, which may be affecting the home situation, and not until all the facts concerning any individual case have been evaluated should a particular disposition be recommended. Only with continued open-minded and thoughtful research, however, shall we be able to distinguish more clearly the significant factors involved in the relationship between early experience and subsequent development and, as a result, to delineate more fully and in greater detail the logical steps toward adequate prevention and treatment of consequent emotional disorders.

REFERENCES

1. Aichhorn, A. (1925) *Wayward youth*, New York, Viking Press (rev. ed., 1951)

2. Allee, W. C. (1938) *The social life of animals*, New York, Norton

3. Bakwin, H. (1942) Loneliness in infants. *Amer. J. Dis. Child.*, **63**, 30

4. Bakwin, H. (1949) Emotional deprivation in infants. *J. Pediat.*, **35**, 512

5. Bender, L. & Yarnell, H. (1941) An observation nursery. *Amer. J. Psychiat.*, **97**, 1158

6. Benedek, T. (1956) Toward the biology of the depressive constellation. *J. Amer. psychoanal. Ass.*, **4**, 389

7. Beres, D. & Obers, S. J. (1950) *The effects of extreme deprivation in infancy on psychic structure in adolescence: a study in ego development*. In: *Psychoanalytic study of the child*, New York, International Universities Press, Vol. 5, p. 212

8. Bergmann, P. & Escalona, S. (1949) *Unusual sensitivities in very young children.* In: *Psychoanalytic study of the child*, New York, International Universities Press, Vol. 3-4, p. 333

9. Beverly, B. I. (1936) Effect of illness on emotional development. *J. Pediat.*, **8**, 533

10. Bowlby, J. (1940) The influence of early environment in the development of neurosis and neurotic character. *Int. J. Psycho-Anal.*, **21**, 154

11. Bowlby, J. (1952) *Maternal care and mental health*, 2nd ed., Geneva (*World Health Organization: Monograph Series*, No. 2)

12. Bowlby, J. (1953) Some pathological processes set in train by early mother-child separation. *J. ment. Sci.*, **99**, 265

13. Bowlby, J. (1958) The nature of the child's tie to his mother. *Int. J. Psycho-Anal.*, **39**, 350

14. Bowlby, J., Ainsworth, M., Boston, M. & Rosenbluth, D. (1956) The effects of mother-child separation: a follow-up study. *Brit. J. med. Psychol.*, **29**, 211

15. Brenneman, J. (1932) The infant ward. *Amer. J. Dis. Child.*, **43**, 577

16. Brody, S. (1956) *Patterns of mothering: maternal influence during infancy*, New York, International Universities Press

17. Brontë, C. (1847) *Jane Eyre*, London, Smith, Elder

18. Bruch, H. (1958) *Obesity*. In: *Symposium on behavior disorders*, in *Pediatric clinics of North America*, New York, Saunders, p. 613

19. Burlingham, D. & Freud, A. (1944) *Infants without families*, London, Allen & Unwin

20. Caplan, G. (1953) *Clinical observations on the emotional life of children in the communal settlements in Israel*. In: Senn, M. J. E., ed., *Problems of infancy and childhood. Transactions of the Seventh Conference*, New York, Josiah Macy Jr Foundation, p. 73

21. Chapin, H. D. (1908) A plan for dealing with atrophic infants and children. *Arch. Pediat.*, **25**, 491

22. Clarke, A. D. B. & Clarke, A. M. (1959) Recovery from the effects of deprivation. *Acta psychol.*, **16**, 137

23. Dennis, W. (1938) Infant development under conditions of restricted practice and of minimum social stimulation: a preliminary report. *J. gen. Psychol.*, **53**, 149

24. Deutsch, F. (1939) The choice of organ in organ neurosis. *Int. J. Psycho-Anal.*, **20**, 252

25. Dickens, C. (1838-39) *Oliver Twist*, London, Bentley

26. Du Pan, R. M. & Roth, S. (1955) The psychological development of a group of children brought up in a hospital type residential nursery. *J. Pediat.*, **47**, 124

27. Edelston, H. (1943) Separation anxiety in young children: study of hospital cases. *Genet. Psychol. Monogr.*, **28**, 3

28. Eissler, K. R. (1950) *Ego-psychological implications of the psychoanalytic treatment of delinquents*. In: *Psychoanalytic study of the child*, New York, International Universities Press, Vol. 5, p. 97

29. Engel, G., Reichsman, F. & Segal, H. (1956) A study of an infant with a gastric fistula: I. Behavior and the rate of total hydrochloric acid secretion. *Psychosom. Med.*, **18**, 374

30. Faust, O. (1952) *Reducing emotional trauma in hospitalized children: a study in psychosomatic pediatrics.* In: Albany Medical College, Departments of Pediatrics and Anesthesiology, *Reducing emotional trauma in hospitalized children,* Albany, p. 13

31. Fischer, L. K. (1952) Hospitalism in six-month-old infants. *Amer. J. Orthopsychiat.,* **22,** 522

32. Freud, S. (1920) *A general introduction to psychoanalysis,* New York, Boni & Liveright

33. Fries, M. E. (1944) Some psychosomatic relationships between mother and infant. *Psychosomat. Med.,* **6,** 159

34. Gesell, A. & Amatruda, C. S. (1954) *Developmental diagnosis,* 2nd ed., New York, Hoeber

35. Glaser, K. & Eisenberg, L. (1956) Maternal deprivation. *Pediatrics,* **18,** 626

36. Goldfarb, W. (1943) Infant rearing and problem behavior. *Amer. J. Orthopsychiat.,* **13,** 249

37. Goldfarb, W. (1955) *Emotional and intellectual consequences of psychologic deprivation in infancy: a re-evaluation.* In: Hoch, P. & Zubin, J., ed., *Psychopathology of childhood,* New York, Grune & Stratton, p. 192

38. Greene, W. A., jr (1958) Role of a vicarious object in the adaptation to object loss. *Psychosom. Med.,* **20,** 344

39. Harlow, H. F. (1958) The nature of love. *Amer. Psychologist,* **13,** 673

40. Heinecke, C. M. (1956) Some effects of separating two-year-old children from their parents: a comparative study. *Hum. Relat.,* **9,** 105

41. Jackson, E. B. (1942) Treatment of the young child in the hospital. *Amer. J. Orthopsychiat.,* **12,** 56

42. Jacobsen, E. (1954) *The self and the object world: vicissitudes of their infantile cathexes and their influence on ideational and affective development.* In: *Psychoanalytic study of the child,* New York, International Universities Press, Vol. 9, p. 75

43. Jessner, L., Blom, G. & Waldfogel, S. (1952) *Emotional implications of tonsillectomy and adenoidectomy on children.* In: *Psychoanalytic study of the child,* New York, International Universities Press, Vol. 7, p. 126

44. Johnson, A. (1949) *Sanctions for superego lacunae of adolescents.* In: Eissler, K. R., ed., *Searchlights on delinquency,* New York, International Universities Press, p. 225

45. Kanner, L. (1943) Autistic disturbance of affective contact. *Nerv. Child.,* **2,** 217

46. Langford, W. S. (1948) Physical illness and convalescence: their meaning to the child. *J. Pediat.,* **33,** 242

47. Levy, D. (1937) Primary affect hunger. *Amer. J. Psychiat.,* **94,** 643

48. Levy, D. (1943) *Maternal overprotection,* New York, Columbia University Press

49. Levy, D. (1945) Psychic trauma of operations in children, and a note on combat neurosis. *Amer. J. Dis. Child.,* **69,** 7

50. Lewis, H. (1954) *Deprived children (the Mershal experiment). A social and clinical study,* London, Oxford University Press

51. Lippman, H. (1949) *Difficulties encountered in the psychiatric treatment of chronic juvenile delinquents.* In: Eissler, K. R., ed., *Searchlights on delinquency,* International Universities Press, p. 156

52. Lorenz, K. Z. (1950) *The comparative method in studying innate behaviour patterns.* In: Danielli, J. F. & Brown, R., ed., *Physiological mechanisms in animal behaviour,* London, Cambridge University Press (*Symp. Soc. exp. Biol.,* No. 4), p. 112

53. Lourie, R. S. (1955) *Experience with therapy of psychosomatic problems in infants.* In: Hoch, P. H. & Zubin, J., ed., *Psychopathology of childhood,* New York, Grune & Stratton

54. Lowrey, L. G. (1940) Personality distortion and early institutional care. *Amer. J. Orthopsychiat.,* **10,** 576

55. Maenchen, A. (1953) *Notes on early ego disturbances.* In: *The psychoanalytic study of the child,* New York, International Universities Press, Vol. 8, p. 262

56. Mahler, M. S. (1952) *On child psychosis and schizophrenia: autistic and symbiotic infantile psychoses.* In: *Psychoanalytic study of the child,* New York, International Universities Press, Vol. 7, p. 286

57. Moncrieff, A. (1951) Social pediatrics. *Courrier,* **1,** No. 3, 3

58. O'Connor, N. (1956) The evidence for the permanently disturbing effects of mother-child separation. *Acta psychol.,* **12,** 174

59. Orlansky, H. (1949) Infant care and personality. *Psychol. Bull.,* **46,** 1

60. Pease, D. & Gardner, D. B. (1958) Research on the effects of noncontinuous mothering. *Child Develpm.,* **29,** 141

61. Powdermaker, F., Levis, H. T. & Touraine, S. (1937) Psychopathology and treatment of delinquent girls. *Amer. J. Orthopsychiat.,* **7,** 58

62. Provence, S. & Coleman, R. (1957) Environmental retardation (hospitalism) in infants living in families. *Pediatrics,* **19,** 285

63. Prugh, D. G. (1951) The influence of emotional factors on the clinical course of ulcerative colitis in children. *Gastroenterology,* **18,** 339

64. Prugh, D. G. (1951) A preliminary report on the role of emotional factors in idiopathic celiac disease. *Psychosom. Med.,* **13,** 220

65. Prugh, D. G., Staub, E., Sands, H., Kirchsbaum, R. & Lenihan, E. A. (1953) A study of the emotional reactions of children and families to hospitalization and illness. *Amer. J. Orthopsychiat.,* **23,** 70

66. Rank, B. (1949) Adaptation of the psychoanalytic technique for the treatment of young children with atypical development. *Amer. J. Orthopsychiat.,* **19,** 130

67. Rank, B., Putnam, M. & Rochlin, G. (1948) The significance of the " emotional climate " in early feeding difficulties. *Psychosom. Med.,* **10,** 279

68. Ribble, M. (1943) *The rights of infants,* New York, Columbia University Press

69. Richmond, J. B., Eddy, E. & Greer, M. (1958) Rumination, a psychosomatic syndrome of infancy. *Pediatrics,* **22,** 49

70. Robertson, J. (1953) *A two-year-old goes to hospital* (Film: 16 mm; 45 min.; sound. Distributors: Tavistock Child Development Research Unit, London; New York University Film Library; United Nations. Geneva)

71. Robertson, J. (1958) *Young children in hospital*, London, Tavistock Publications

72. Roudinesco, D., David, M. & Nicholas, J. (1952) Responses of young children to separation from their mothers. *Courrier*, 2, No. 2, 66

73. Schaffer, H. R. (1958) Objective observations of personality development in early infancy. *Brit. J. med. Psychol.*, 31, 174

74. Seitz, P. D. (1954) Effects of infantile experience upon adult behavior in animal subjects: I. Effects of litter size during infancy upon adult behavior in the rat. *Amer J. Psychiat.*, 110, 916

75. Senn, M. J. E. (1945) Emotional aspects of convalescence. *Child (Wash.)*, 10, 24

76. Sperling, M. (1949) The role of the mother in psychosomatic disorders in children. *Psychosom. Med.*, 11, 377

77. Spitz, R. (1945) *Hospitalism*. In: *Psychoanalytic study of the child*, New York, International Universities Press, Vol. 1, p. 53

78. Spitz, R. (1951) *The psychogenic diseases in infancy: an attempt at their etiologic classification*. In: *Psychoanalytic study of the child*, New York, International Universities Press, Vol. 6, p. 255

79. Spitz, R. & Wolf, K. M. (1946) *Anaclitic depression*. In: *Psychoanalytic study of the child*, New York, International Universities Press, Vol. 2, p. 313

80. Theis, S. van S. (1924) *How foster children turn out*, New York, State Charities Aid Association (Publication No. 165)

81. Wallace, M. & Feinauer, V. (1948) Understanding a sick child's behavior. *Amer. J. Nursing*, 48, 517

PATERNAL AND MATERNAL ROLES AND DELINQUENCY

R. G. ANDRY *

The purpose of this chapter is twofold: to examine critically the concept of " maternal deprivation " and to establish a case for recognizing several additional and perhaps more important concepts, including that of the pathogenic paternal factor in delinquency.

First the general background of the problem including the maternal-deprivation concept will be discussed. The sequence will deal with a selection of findings in a research project conducted by the author and recorded elsewhere in much greater detail.[1]

A CRITICAL EXAMINATION OF THE CONCEPT OF " MATERNAL DEPRIVATION "

The concept of " maternal deprivation ", as brought out clearly by Dr John Bowlby,[4] seems to imply that one of the most dangerous pathogenic factors in child development is the harm that may be done if a child has been deprived of his natural mother's love through separation. This concept, while undoubtedly valid in specific cases, as demonstrated by Bowlby, causes dissatisfaction in several directions, if one wishes to consider the vast and complex development of personality as a whole.

For instance, the concept seems to imply that, other things being equal, a single factor — namely, maternal deprivation — is often the main pathogenic factor in personality development. But is this necessarily so ? For instance, can one ever assume that other things are equal ? Might it not be that child development is so complex (even during the first years when mother-child relationships seem to be more important than father-child and child-sibling relationships) that the relatively crude condition of maternal deprivation may be only one among several other perhaps more important aspects of mother-child relationships ? For instance, what of the child who does not become a delinquent or neurotic — even though he may have suffered maternal deprivation — but who

---

* Psychology Department, University of London Institute of Education, London, England.

was cared for by a warm-hearted mother-substitute such as a relative or a nurse ? Or what of the child who has become a delinquent or neurotic, despite the fact that he was never maternally deprived during the critical periods in his life ? What of stimulating institutions such as the *Kibbutzim*, where maternally deprived children do not seem to become delinquents ? The delinquency of such children in other institutions may well be due to the questionable quality of the institution.

Often the distinction between physical and psychological separation seems to be overlooked. The concept of maternal deprivation appears to imply that physical separation between mother and child is usually very damaging to the child's proper development. But what of the case where physical separation has not occurred, but where psychological separation seems to have acted as a major pathogenic factor in the subtle way called by the Gluecks [15] " broken-under-the-roof relationships " ? Bowlby [3] himself found that only about one-quarter of his delinquents had suffered separation from their mothers to the extent that it appeared to have given rise to the maternal-deprivation syndrome. Similarly, the Gluecks [15] report that of their sample, closely resembling the delinquency population as a whole, again only about one-quarter of the delinquents came from broken homes — i.e., homes where a " mother-child " separation factor had occurred. This point was also taken up by the writer [1] when, in the sample selection of cases for his project, he found that about 25% came from broken homes. The remainder scrutinized for study were also examined to determine whether more subtle " under-the-roof " relationships had occurred which could be traced back to forms of physical separation rather than to breakdowns in psychological communication between the child and his parents. This point will be taken up again further on.

So far, then, the maternal-deprivation concept appears to be vulnerable in several directions as a central pathogenic agent. Briefly, the concept is vulnerable on the following grounds:

(1)   Is it valid or expedient to isolate a single factor, such as maternal deprivation, from the complex matrix of human personality development to account for pathological behaviour ?

(2)   Is it valid to take such a single concept and to regard it as a central pathogenic agent giving rise to such diverse behaviour patterns as psychosis, psychoneurosis, and delinquency ? (Most forensic psychologists — for example, Bennett [2] and Glover [14] — do not regard the majority of delinquents as neurotics.)

(3)   To what extent is it profitable to regard such a concept as being of sufficient significance to account for the major part of deviant behaviour ?

(4) How far is it useful to explain, through such a concept, a behaviourally deviant pattern in terms of a theory (Kleinian psycho-analytic) which is heavily committed to certain viewpoints, one being that child-mother relationships during the early crucial years of a child's development are usually more basic than other, later, child-object relationships — between the child and his father, other siblings, social environmental challenges — and original genetic endowment backed by biochemically responding conditions?

(5) How far are designs of experiments satisfactory and valid in establishing the importance of the maternal-deprivation syndrome?

It is not intended, here, to discuss each of these five points exhaustively, but to examine their general validity, the usefulness of the concept of maternal deprivation, and the value of this concept within the framework of current psychological theories.

Regarding the general question of validity and the design of experiments, it seems desirable to consider whether Bowlby and the maternal-deprivation theorists have established the case that the concept is both veritable and useful, and that it was isolated through rigorously controlled experiments.

Generally speaking, a necessary condition for the validity of any major concept is not only that experiments must show the concept (for instance, maternal deprivation) to be primarily responsible for a set of behaviour, but also that this can be demonstrated repeatedly and consistently on later occasions. It must also be shown that other variables have not been mainly responsible for the same set of behaviour (e.g., delinquency). Only thus could a single concept stand revealed as a major etiological variable. Usually, in this kind of work (as Vernon [30] and Mannheim & Wilkins [21] show) a "factor-analysis" should reveal quickly how much of the total "variance" is accounted for by major factors. The maternal-deprivation factor should thus have a high factor loading (and account for most of the variance) in relation to other variables, if the factor is to be accepted as being of primary importance. Unfortunately maternal-deprivation theorists have not presented their evidence in factor-analysis terms.

The onus of proof is on the maternal-deprivation theorist to demonstrate that a set of behaviour (such as delinquency, or an "affectionless character" or neuroticism) is *primarily* due to separation having occurred between a mother and her child during a particular span of his age. Have the maternal-deprivation theorists succeeded in this demonstration? Bowlby [4] bases much of his thesis on his own work with forty-four juvenile thieves, and on the works of Theis, Beres, Obers, Bender, Goldfarb, Spitz, and others.

His own study suggests that maternal deprivation is a useful concept and capable of being isolated in about one-quarter of his cases; however, it seems to have a particularly pernicious influence in those described as " affectionless characters ". It should not be overlooked that Bowlby [3] himself, in his own study, never went beyond the reasonable position that delinquency is not primarily based on a maternal-deprivation factor, but that a specialized sub-group among delinquents (the psychopathic affectionless character) has largely suffered from the maternal-deprivation factor. This agrees with other views, from Burt [9] to the Gluecks,[15] who find that delinquency is the result of more than one factor. Would Dr Bowlby agree that, apart from its limited aspect, maternal deprivation plays no great part in the majority of delinquent cases, nor in the majority of cases of neuroticism (a condition not specifically investigated in Bowlby's forty-four juvenile thieves from the point of view of maternal deprivation)?

Bowlby, in his monograph,[4] accepts the finding in the well-controlled studies of Theis and Beres & Obers that hereditary factors can in all probability be ruled out as the major responsible pathological factor, thus exposing the maternal-deprivation factor as vitally important. In recent years, however, experimental evidence suggests that the whole question of genetic inheritance needs examining once more. This can no longer be quickly dismissed as being of minor importance vis-à-vis such environmental factors as maternal deprivation. Tinbergen,[29] Lorenz,[20] Harlow,[16] Bowlby [5] himself, and especially W. Kessen,* in the child development field, have re-opened this issue. For instance, Kessen at Yale, in filming the sucking and other responses of babies from birth through the first week of their lives, found that, often irrespective of the mother's feeding attitude towards her child, the infants displayed characteristic motivational patterns of their own, some being very responsive towards the mother, others considerably less so. It goes without saying that the practical implications of this finding are important and may help to explain the statements of mothers who point out the differences in " responsiveness pattern " since earliest childhood between a delinquent (or neurotic) child of theirs and a non-delinquent (or non-neurotic) sibling.

Since the publication of his monograph, Bowlby [5] himself seems to have developed a growing interest in the field of inheritance, as shown in his more recent papers on the inherited clinging response of monkeys. From this, however, it is not clear whether he would accept the position that much of what in the past might have been attributed to an environmentally induced maternal-deprivation pathology factor might be due to

---

* Research currently being conducted at Yale University (as yet unpublished).

the more fundamental inherited cortical and genetic structure of certain individuals. Here one wonders to what extent he shares Eysenck's [12] view that differences in personality patterns are relatable to a theory of cortical inhibition and disinhibition. This implies, for instance, that the major origin of delinquency need not be sought in factors such as maternal deprivation, but in factors such as, for example, how relatively unconditionable a delinquent is, as revealed by his limited extent of being conditionable under certain Pavlovian testing situations. It is interesting to note that Bowlby,[6] in a recent publication on the etiology of mourning and the depressive position, departs somewhat from the orthodox basis of Freud,[13] Melanie Klein [18] and Burlingham & Freud [8] and comes nearer to positions held by academic psychologists such as Miller & Dollard,[22] Mowrer [23] and Shoben.[27] In their view, not a single, but several, measurable interacting variables of different habit strengths account for a given set of behaviour. Also of interest are Wilkins' findings,[31] which suggest the delinquency proneness of a child during his fifth year under traumatic conditions. By that time and at that age the single maternal-deprivation factor is not likely to have operated.

Bowlby [4] accepted in his original monograph the point made by Obers, Bender, Goldfarb and Spitz about the seeming irreversibility of the maternal-deprivation concept, once this factor had been demonstrated. The question, as Lady Wootton rightly points out elsewhere in this volume (see page 68), is whether these cases were sufficiently followed up, and whether life-correcting factors, such as successfully contracted marriages, may not have demonstrated the reversibility potential of maternally deprived cases.

Returning to the central theme of the existence and relative importance of the maternal-deprivation factor, Bowlby [4] made his own interest clear in his monograph by regarding the concept as being of considerable importance in the understanding of deviant behaviour such as delinquency and neuroticism. However, the results of more recent investigations tend to show, if anything, the reverse — namely, the relative unimportance of the maternal-deprivation factor in the majority of cases of deviant behaviour. Naess,[24] who matched delinquent with non-delinquent brothers (holding the age factor as a constant), found that separation had occurred more among non-delinquents than delinquents. Dr Hilda Lewis,[19] in her study of 500 children at a reception centre, was unable to demonstrate a clear connexion between a child's separation from his mother and a particular pattern of disturbed child behaviour. Neither was O'Connor [25] able to demonstrate any permanently disturbing effects of mother-child separation. Similarly, Stott [28] and especially A. D. B. & A. M. Clarke [10] bring out the reversibility of the effects, in cases where a separation effect seems to have been active, by demonstrating that, under proper institutional care, damaging effects can be relieved, and also that, under improper institutional care, the behavioural disturbances manifesting themselves are due less to a maternal-deprivation effect than to poor institutional care. Moreover, the Clarkes [10] observed the damaging effects over a period of time of bad institutionalization on the intellectual functioning of children.

It should, however, be noted that, since the appearance of his monograph, Bowlby has modified some of his views regarding the perniciousness and influence of the maternal-deprivation effect. (This can be seen in the follow-up of the findings of Bowlby, Ainsworth, Boston & Rosenbluth.[7]) Also, since his association with Dr Heinecke [17] in 1952, he has demonstrated the advantage of longitudinal over cross-sectional studies in this field.

The works of Douglas & Blomfield [11] and Rowntree [26] concerning the alleged existence and usefulness of the maternal-deprivation concept must also be mentioned here. Rowntree investigated *post hoc* 277 children up to four years of age who by then had suffered the absence of a parent, and matched them with children from stable homes. She concluded that most of the deprived children were not exceptionally prone to the grosser forms of emotional disturbance. Rowntree,[26] who also matched 4668 infants who were separated with non-separated ones in the same neighbourhood, had, up to the time of publication of her study, been unable to find many significant correlations in favour of the maternal deprivation theory. Similarly, Andry [1] was unable to isolate clearly any pathogenic maternal-deprivation factor. By matching 80 delinquents with 80 non-delinquents (boys between the ages of 11 and 15 and a subsample of both parents) he devised an interview questionnaire in order to find out which child had been deprived — that is, separated specifically either from his mother (as distinct from his father) or from both parents (as measured by whether the child was evacuated with or without his mother or his father, etc.). Again, he was unable to establish clearly among his delinquent sample that they had suffered, by comparison with his matched non-delinquents, any unusual degree of separation from their mothers. A more detailed discussion of the author's findings will be given later.

In summing up the first part of this chapter, all that need be said is that Bowlby's maternal-deprivation concept, though useful in certain cases, is probably not to be found as universally as was suspected by many shortly after the appearance of his stimulating monograph. Since then, he and others have had second thoughts on the matter, in varying degree, without repudiating the essentials where appropriate. The author of this chapter makes a special plea for the recognition of the role played by the father, in addition to that of the mother, as far as child development is concerned. Also he hereby appeals to analytically orientated psychologists for a greater recognition and appreciation of the usefulness of the complex " learning-theory models ", which have helped greatly in this field with the understanding of child-parent relationships. It is suggested here that the two kinds of models (the psychoanalytic and the learning-theory ones) need not be antagonistic to each other; on the contrary, with patience and tolerance, they can prove to be complementary.

RESEARCH ON THE PATHOGENIC ROLE OF FATHERS IN DELINQUENCY

Andry,[1] in an endeavour to investigate aspects of child-parent relationships, approached the topic essentially from two angles. He set out to examine the boys' relationship, in his study of 80 delinquent and 80 non-delinquent boys, not only their mothers but also with their fathers. Also, he examined aspects of child-parent separations in order to study the relative importance of mother-and-child and of father-and-child separations. This seemed desirable, since the maternal-deprivation theorists seem to have grossly neglected the concomitant role of the father.

Concerning the topic of separations, the author found it necessary to distinguish (contrary to the practice of most maternal-deprivation theorists) three possible aspects of parent-child separation:

(1) psychological separation as a concomitant of physical separation (it is this aspect which is primarily considered by maternal-deprivation theorists; however, it appears essential to consider also the following two aspects);

(2) psychological separation without physical separation;

(3) physical separation without concomitant psychological separation.

It should be noted that the maternal-deprivation theorists concentrate on the hypothesis of mother-child psychological separation as a consequence of mother-child physical separation. It was felt that this was too restrictive and therefore to study this hypothesis further one should also link it with a father-child separation factor. Consequently, it was found necessary to distinguish three possible forms of parent-child separation:

(1) separation of the child from its mother only (or maternal separation);

(2) separation of the child from its father only (or paternal separation);

(3) separation of the child from both of its parents (or dual-parental separation).

Maternal-deprivation theorists seem to ignore the possible importance of paternal and dual-parental separations.

Owing to the fact that the author's study was not longitudinal but cross-sectional, it was not possible to trace in detail all Bowlby's valuable criteria for the maternal-deprivation factor, which tends to depend on: (1) the child's age when separation occurred; (2) the length of the separation; (3) the degree of the separation; (4) the frequency of the separation; (5) the quality of the parent-child relationships before separation occurred; (6) the experience of the child with its parent-substitute; (7) the child's reception by its parents when reunited with them. However, the author decided to determine what sorts of physical separation characterized the three basic forms of parent-child physical separation (i.e., maternal, paternal and dual-parental). The oft-quoted adverse effect of child institutionalization had to be expanded on logical grounds. For instance, wartime evacuations involved the separation of the child not only from his mother but also from his father. The author therefore selected for study various kinds of separation of the child in relation not only to his mother but also to his father or to both parents.

In order to get " pure " maternal-separation items the samples were checked for differences between delinquents and non-delinquents in relation to: (a) whether mothers were working, and (b) whether mothers had been hospitalized. In order to get " pure " paternal-separation items the samples were similarly checked for: (a) those fathers who had been away on war service and who had delinquent children, and those fathers who, although they had been away on war service, had non-delinquent children; (b) whether a child had been evacuated with the mother (thus having been paternally deprived); (c) whether fathers had been away a great deal on shift work during the boys' childhood; (d) whether fathers had been hospitalized during the boy's childhood. Lastly, in order to get " pure " dual-parental-separation items, it was decided to inquire into differences between the samples from the point of view of: (a) whether the child had been evacuated by himself; (b) whether the child had been hospitalized; (c) whether both parents had been hospitalized (thus possibly producing a dual-parental deprivation effect). All these questions were, of course, correlated with the age of the child during which ill-effects might have developed. Thus attempts were made to cover Bowlby's criteria (1), (2) and (4) (see above). Regarding the other criteria (concerning the quality of child-parent relationships before and after separation), the problem had to be approached differently (as will be shown later) — namely, in a more general way, based on the fundamental affective relationship between a child and his parents. The results proved of interest.

It was found that no statistically significant differences between the two samples emerged in connexion with the hypothesis that there is a greater tendency for delinquents to have suffered maternal separation than for non-delinquents. Thus, the hypothesis that delinquents suffered more from maternal separation than non-delinquents had to be rejected, at least on the basis of the items under investigation. Somewhat similar results emerged in connexion with the hypothesis that there is a greater tendency for delinquents to have suffered paternal separation than for non-delinquents. No significant differences emerged in respect of either (a) the father's absence from home due to war service, or (b) the boys having been evacuated with their mothers. Delinquents, on the basis of these items in this research, cannot therefore be said to have suffered more than non-delinquents, during the first few years of their lives, from paternal separation. (It was later demonstrated by the author, however, that although no adverse paternal-separation factor in early childhood was demonstrable, it was in fact possible to demonstrate the existence of disturbed child-father relationships irrespective of whether early paternal-separation factors had occurred.) Further, in keeping with these results, the hypothesis that there is a greater tendency for delinquents to have suffered from dual-parental separation than for non-delinquents proved negative. This finding was based on such questions as: " Was the child evacuated by himself ? " " How old was he then ? " " What illnesses necessitated his hospitalization for more than one week during the first three years of his life ? " " When and for how long were the parents hospitalized and thus separated from the child ? " Generally speaking then, it was found that although the technique used was blunt and of necessity inferior to a more reliable direct observation study, the results failed to support the maternal-deprivation theory. It must be kept in mind that the findings can neither validate nor invalidate the maternal-deprivation theory. However, they do call the general usefulness of this theory into question, because :

(1)   to be of heuristic value, a theory must incorporate clearly defined empirical referents and must be susceptible to empirical testing by a practical research method operating on these referents;

(2)   apart from the fact that the maternal-deprivation theory does not satisfactorily provide clearly enough defined empirical referents, it is not, in certain crucial respects, susceptible to empirical testing by a *practical* research method (as the findings presented briefly above testify).

In order to prove the pathogenicity of the paternal-deprivation factor, several things would be necessary. Techniques would have to be evolved for an on-the-spot observation and a long-term study covering the child during, say, the first twenty years of his life. The sample would have to be large, in order to ensure that a statistically adequate sample of delinquents would emerge, and the study would have to consider the roles of both parents — not merely that of the mother.

So far then, it is recalled that the author approaches his conceptionalization in a twofold way, with regard to child-parent attitudes and to character formation. However, it was felt that an investigation of child-parent separation, though going beyond the maternal-deprivation concept by taking paternal deprivation into consideration, was still not going far enough. Consequently, the other approach was conceptionalized in wider terms. It was reasoned that, in order to do full justice to the study of child behaviour (or misbehaviour), it would be necessary to relate findings to aspects of the study of the personality formation of an individual as a whole and, if possible, to relate this to already existing personality theory in psychology and not necessarily within the more specific confines of psychoanalysis. Consequently, the nearest model at hand seemed that of role perception. The task seemed to be to try to find out something about a child's perception of the relative importance of the roles played in his life by his mother and his father (and to check with both parents the extent to which this seemed to approximate to the true state of affairs as seen from the parent's point of view). With this in mind, the execution of the task became relatively easy.

As mentioned earlier, a sample of delinquent and non-delinquent boys were interviewed by means of a specially designed interview questionnaire covering a series of areas which presumably seemed important in their lives from the point of view of their character formation and overt behaviour. The major areas selected, in addition to the early childhood developmental ones already mentioned above (which presumably equally merited investigation though they affected the boys not before but during the so-called "latency period" and thereafter), were these: (1) emotional atmosphere, and (2) training. Under each of these headings several sub-areas seemed in need of investigation. The basic theme of the inquiry was centred on the area of parent-child affection. Which parent did the child feel more loved by — the mother or the father? Or did he feel that both loved him equally or that neither loved him? One of the tasks was to establish whether among the delinquent boys a greater proportion felt more loved by their mothers or by their fathers. This seemed important to find out. The research had already shown that, as far as one could tell, no deprivation effects (either maternal, paternal, or dual-parental) due to separation had occurred. Therefore, what other faulty child-parent relationships were at work possibly to account in part for the delinquent behaviour? Did the delinquent feel in some subtle way rejected by the mother? — as one might suspect if one kept in mind the implications of the maternal-deprivation concept. Interestingly enough, research findings tended to suggest the contrary. Among the delinquents there was a preponderance of those who implied that they felt rejected by their fathers (indicating that they felt loved more by their mothers, whereas the non-delinquents indicated with much greater constancy that they felt loved equally by both parents).

This pattern of the father-rejected delinquent tended to appear in a number of areas and sub-areas which were investigated. It emerged also in the child-parent communication area. Here attempts were made to assess both environmental and psychological communication between a child and his parents. Was the mother or the father more often away on shift work? And had such absences occurred more among the delinquents, having perhaps contributed to delinquency? Or, which parent did the boy feel more understood by—the mother or the father? To whom did he first turn when in trouble, and which parent did he prefer to deal with if under stress? Results showed that the bulk of the delinquents tended, by comparison with the non-delinquents, to stay away from both parents and not to seek their advice when in trouble. Further, it was found that both groups tended, if anything, to seek out their mothers before their fathers. However, thereafter, quantitative differences emerged again in the two groups. The delinquents in response to the question " Which parent do you prefer ultimately and finally to deal with your case if you have done something wrong? " opted for their mothers, whereas the non-delinquents opted for their fathers, in the hope of thereby getting the matter finally disposed of. Presumably the communication channels were worse between the delinquents and their fathers than in the case of the non-delinquents, and the proportion of delinquents who were more afraid of their fathers than their mothers was greater than that of the non-delinquents. Similarly, when aspects of the home climate were investigated the relative paternal glumness as opposed to maternal cheerfulness was commented upon more by the delinquents than by the non-delinquents.

Fathers were very similarly incriminated when the investigation applied to the field of " training " and punishments. Linked with the earlier area of an inquiry into child-parent affection two assumptions were made : (*a*) that adequate rapport must exist between parents and child so that the child feels sufficiently loved by his parents to make him feel the need for (to find meaning in) socialization training and learning; and (*b*) that a consistent mode of training must be adopted which is based more on the positive approach of praise and reward than on the negative one of punishment. Consequently, a series of hypotheses were set up in order to see whether a clear source of authority

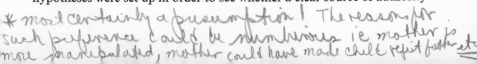

most certainly a presumption! The reasons for such preference could be numerous ie mother is more manipulated, mother could have made child reject father etc

existed in the family and, if so, from which parent this emanated; how each of the parents reacted in the case of delinquents and non-delinquents to " trouble "; how " reasonably " a child interpreted a parent's reaction to trouble caused by the child; how strict parents were and whether they praised positive behaviour rather than punished negative behaviour. Among the many findings only a few are mentioned here. For instance, with regard to clear sources of authority in the home, it was found that non-delinquents had a very strong tendency to recognize their fathers as the head of the family and obeyed them most. Delinquents, however, though recognizing their fathers as heads of households, tended to obey them least. This points to a greater degree of defective paternal leadership among delinquents than among non-delinquents. ✳

It should be mentioned that attempts were made, with reference to the major areas under investigation, to compile an agreement code by asking both parents to answer the same questions as their sons. All too often in child-guidance investigations one finds that, if control groups are used at all, parents are not often enough asked to supply answers to the same questions which have been asked of the child, and that if this is done it is the mothers who are questioned rather than the fathers. In this instance both the father and the mother were examined, separately from each other and from their sons. The aim was to discover whether a delinquent's opinion as to his parents' feelings towards him — for example, that he felt loved more by his mother than by his father — would be confirmed by either parent. Originally it was hypothesized that there would be great discrepancies between answers, and that many parents, especially those who felt guilty about their defective relationships with their children, would tend to give answers diametrically opposed to those of their sons. It was interesting to find that the unexpected happened. On the whole there was a remarkable amount of agreement between the answers of the parents and those of their children, in both groups, even if a child had by implication exposed the father, say, as the one who was the less loving of the two parents. This tends to indicate the pathetic fact that parents, and especially the oft-mentioned inadequate father, were aware of deficiencies and yet were powerless to do much about ameliorating the situation. This would lead one to recommend that, in future child-guidance work, not only the mothers, but also more and more of the fathers should be involved in the whole treatment programme, especially in the case of delinquents. In keeping with this, the author already had the occasion, some years ago in Australia, to conduct an experimental clinic for the fathers of delinquent boys, with exceptionally good results.

In summing up the second part of this chapter a few general comments should be made. First, the many obvious limitations which stem from

✳ perhaps

a pilot study of this kind are recognized and the author would be the last to let his thesis rest here. In fact, further projects, especially those including delinquent girls, are being planned. Secondly, it is intended to help to redress the balance a little by pointing out, with the findings of this research, the defective role frequently played by the father and not only that of the all-too-often mentioned mother. Thirdly, it is not intended thus to overemphasize the often defective role of the father to the exclusion of that of the mother. Finally, the purpose is to emphasize the subtle and basic triangularity which exists (from a child's point of view) between a child and both his parents, a relationship which is subjected to constant frustrations among all concerned, be it through the arrival of other siblings or through each member of the triad failing to respond appropriately to the others' needs and failing to learn and to become conditioned to a multitude of situations throughout a lifetime within a cultural and subcultural setting.

REFERENCES

1. Andry, R. G. (1960) *Delinquency and parental pathology*, London, Methuen

2. Bennett, I. (1960) *Delinquent and neurotic children*, London, Tavistock Publications

3. Bowlby, J. (1946) *Forty-four juvenile thieves, their characters and home life*, London, Baillière, Tindall & Cox

4. Bowlby, J. (1952) *Maternal care and mental health*, 2nd ed., Geneva (*World Health Organization: Monograph Series*, No. 2)

5. Bowlby, J. (1958) The nature of the child's tie to his mother. *Int. J. Psycho-Anal.*, **39**, 350

6. Bowlby, J. (1961) Processes of mourning. *Bull. Brit. Psychol. Soc.*, **43**, 56

7. Bowlby, J., Ainsworth, M., Boston, M. & Rosenbluth, D. (1956) The effects of mother-child separation: a follow-up study. *Brit. J. med. Psychol.*, **29**, 211

8. Burlingham, D. & Freud, A. (1943) *Infants without families*, London, Allen & Unwin

9. Burt, C. (1944) *The young delinquent*, 4th ed., London, University of London Press

10. Clarke, A. D. B. & Clarke, A. M. (1959) Recovery from the effects of deprivation *Acta psychol.*, **16**, 137

11. Douglas, W. B. & Blomfield, J. M. (1958) *Children under five*, London, Allen & Unwin

12. Eysenck, H. J., ed. (1960) *Handbook of abnormal psychology*, London, Pitman

13. Freud, S. (1933) *New introductory lectures in psycho-analysis*, New York, Norton

14. Glover, E. (1959) *The roots of crime*, New York, International Universities Press

15. Glueck, S. & Glueck, E. T. (1950) *Unraveling juvenile delinquency*, Boston, Mass., Harvard University Press

16. Harlow, H. F. (1958) The nature of love. *Amer. Psychologist*, **13**, 673

17. Heinecke, C. M. (1956) Some effects of separating two-year-old children from their parents. *Hum. Relat.*, **9**, 105

18. Klein, M. (1923) The development of a child. *Int. J. Psycho-Anal.*, **4**, 419

19. Lewis, H. (1954) *Deprived children (the Mershal experiment). A social and clinical study*, London, Oxford University Press

20. Lorenz, K. Z. (1950) *The comparative method in studying innate behaviour patterns* In: Danielli, J. F. & Brown, R., ed., *Physiological mechanisms in animal behaviour*, London, Cambridge University Press (*Symp. Soc. exp. Biol.* No. 4), p. 221

21. Mannheim, H. & Wilkins, L. T. (1955) *Prediction methods in relation to Borstal training*, London, H.M. Stationery Office

22. Miller, J. & Dollard, J. (1950) *Personality and psychotherapy*, New York, McGraw-Hill

23. Mowrer, O. H. (1960) *Learning theory and behavior*, New York, Wiley

24. Naess, S. (1959) Mother-child separation and delinquency. *Brit. J. Delinq.*, **10**, 22

25. O'Connor, N. (1956) The evidence for the permanently disturbing effects of mother-child separation. *Acta psychol.*, **12**, 174

26. Rowntree, G. (1955) Early childhood in broken families. *Populat. Stud.*, **8**, 247

27. Shoben, E. J., jr (1949) Psychotherapy as a problem in learning theory. *Psychol. Bull.*, **46**, 366

28. Stott, D. (1956) The effects of separation from the mother in early life. *Lancet*, **1**, 624

29. Tinbergen, N. (1952) " Derived " activities. *Quart. Rev. Biol.*, **27**, 1

30. Vernon, P. E. (1960) *The structure of human abilities*, London, Methuen

31. Wilkins, L. T. (1960) *Delinquent generations*, London, H.M. Stationery Office

A CULTURAL ANTHROPOLOGIST'S APPROACH TO MATERNAL DEPRIVATION

MARGARET MEAD *

Cultural anthropology can contribute in a number of ways to an examination of the series of problems raised by Bowlby and to the further testing of his hypotheses, as discussed in this volume.

Detailed configurations of types of infant care, child-adult relationships and later regularities in personality can be cited, on a comparative basis, from primitive societies such as the Arapesh or Eskimo tribes, from traditional societies such as the Balinese and the Palestinian Arabs, and from specifically experimental societies such as the Hutterites, the Doukobours and the *Kibbutzim* settlers of modern Israel. All these are examples of natural historical experiments in the study of which it is possible to avoid the disadvantages inherent both in the utilization of mass catastrophes (as in evacuations following earthquakes or during warfare) and in experimental set-ups in which really natural "control" situations are never properly approximated. Such comparative studies can be used to widen the terms of reference and reduce the provincialism of studies based only upon modern societies; they can be used as natural control situations and as hypotheses-generating situations. For reasons to be discussed below, primitive societies, while providing the most dramatic materials that may throw light on the biological potentialities involved in parent-child behaviours, are usually unsuitable for the verification of hypotheses, because of the very small number of cases available for detailed study. **

---

* Associate Curator of Ethnology, American Museum of Natural History, New York, USA.

** The most intensive efforts to obtain information on a series of infants over a period of time, such as those made by Bateson and Mead in Bali, [24,34] and by Kluckhohn and co-workers among the Navajo,[15,16] illustrate this deficiency, even in large populations where some of the paraphernalia of modern industrialized societies have been introduced—in the form of some public health measure, such as vaccination, and some record keeping, such as birth registration. In Bali we studied every infant during a year's continuous residence in one village of 500 people, systematically revisited the village during a second year, and paid a short return visit the third year. This systematic attention yielded a total of eight children, whose birth dates were accurately known, who were available for periodic study and who were alive for final photographing, filming and recording in the third year. On a return visit to Bali twenty years later (American Museum of Natural History Second Balinese Expedition, 1957-58, Department of Health, Education and Welfare, National Institute of Mental Health Grant M-2118, " Reconnaissance Recheck on Balinese Mental Health ") specific plans had been made to make a detailed study of the male child of Karba, who had himself been the male child most intensively studied in 1936-39. [2,34] On arriving in the village on 19 December 1957, however, we found that this child had been drowned two days before.

COMPARATIVE STUDIES PROVIDE CORRECTIONS
TO SIMPLISTIC FORMULATIONS

Comparative studies, especially of primitive peoples living under simple conditions of food gathering, hunting and horticulture, provide suggestive materials on the biological potentialities of such practices as the suckling of the child by several women or the use of the dry breasts of young girls, old women or men as comforters; and of situations which would seem to do various types of violence to the organism of mother or child, such as: the effort necessary to evoke milk from a non-lactating woman by keeping an adopted child persistently hungry so that enough suckling pressure is applied to the breast; the suckling of the neonate by a woman who has been suckling her own child for two or three years, with resulting change in the protein content of the breast milk; methods of binding and purposeful deformation of the child's head or whole body; permanent encasement of the child in some cradling device so that there is no contact between the body of the child and that of the mother, except between nipple and mouth; use of extreme methods of weaning including the smearing of the breasts with mud, which is represented to the child as excrement, or banishment of the child to the care of a stranger; the simultaneous suckling of siblings with purposeful stimulation of jealousy in both, etc. There are a great variety of such practices, both briefly reported [30] and in some cases discussed in connexion with detailed studies of " culture and personality", which it would be impossible to set up experimentally today for paediatric and ethical reasons, but which may be observed in a context of completely responsible execution where the primitive people in question believe they are doing the best they can for their children.

The cultural anthropologist deals with whole cultures — under the greatly simplified conditions of absence of a written language and a numerically small society — and is therefore equipped to consider the way in which the whole mesh of human behaviour characteristic of a particular society is reflected in the behaviour of any given individual. This recognition of the complexity of the conditions within which an infant grows, or a given adult-child relationship exists, can be used as a corrective to the present tendency to over-attribute certain consequences to single causes or sequences of events, such as breast-feeding or its absence, separation from a mother-figure, institutionalization, early or late toilet training, swaddling, etc., which has been characteristic of attempts to apply clinical insight to the establishment of viable theory and to the development of comprehensive recommendations for changes in social practice. Failure to take into account the persistent warnings of anthropologists against such single causal sequences has resulted in the stream of claims and counter-claims which have characterized this field in the last twenty years.[4,6,28,29,37] The lack of any such corrective is demonstrated in detail by the review provided in this volume by Prugh & Harlow (see page 9), which fails to take into account a single study in which anthropologists have been involved, or to cite any publications by anthropologists. These authors reach the conclusion that " the child's response to separation, as a representative potential trauma, is a complex process, influenced by its nature and duration, the quality of mothering before and after the experience, the age and stage of development of the child... The influence of other variables such as the inborn or acquired biological capacities of the child are more difficult to assess but must also be considered ". Even in this statement of a complexity which any student of whole cultures would take for granted, there is no allowance for the other complexities introduced by culture itself.

In order that anthropological contributions, both explicit and potential, may be brought to bear on the problem of maternal care and mental health in those respects specifically outlined in Bowlby's monograph, [5] it will be useful to break down his original discussion and that of his commentators into a new set of categories. I should like to distinguish among the following issues:

(1)   The removal of children from the care of familiar people, close relatives, members of the greater families, neighbours, godparents, etc., to impersonal institutions where they are cared for by strangers in a way which prevents the establishment of reliable personal ties.

(2)   Problems arising from breaks in the relationship of a child to its biological mother and father and siblings.

(3)   Problems of the very early hours and days of life and the establishment in the parturient woman, the neonate and the other members of the family of new patterns of relationship resulting from that particular birth.

(4)   Problems of the patterns of relationships over the entire life-span of the individual, in which early patterns of continuity, separation, concentration or diffusion of emotional ties, etc., are reflected in the responses of younger to older, older to younger, and equal to equal.

(5)   Problems attendant upon the attempt to apply the findings of the human sciences, both at the observational and at the clinical level, to preventive mental health practices in the various societies of the world, by altering patterns of hospitalization, by introducing mass measures of other sorts, and by advocating changes in the individual practices of mothers, fathers, teachers, paediatricians, etc.

INSTANCES OF INSTITUTIONAL PRACTICES

It is particularly important to take the institutional questions separately, because there are no comparable situations within the primitive societies in which the cultural anthropologist collects his primary data. All the functions served by institutions — care of the orphan, care of the child of a sick mother, care of the handicapped or defective child, care of the illegitimate child — are dealt with in primitive societies either by care of the child within the greater family or neighbourhood group, on an individual basis which obviates the major trauma-inducing aspect of institutional care — the impersonality of an institution —, or, drastically, by the elimination of the child by such means as burying the newborn child with the dead mother, or exposing immediately or extinguishing by a process of slow, low-level care children who show extreme handicaps. The child who is chosen to live is cared for personally, not impersonally. Our institutions have resulted from a discrepancy between our social conscience — which demands *impersonal* efforts to be made to protect every individual, regardless of whether he be illegitimate, orphaned, a refugee from war or catastrophe whose parents are unknown, or defective, and which demands the construction of services, medical, nursing, custodial, etc., to carry out our impersonal ethical intentions — and our ability to provide adequate, artificially created personal situations within which the children who are saved can be cared for. This discrepancy has become the more conspicuous with the increasing size of modern societies and enhanced communication, which makes the orphaning of children in Korea or Dahomey a matter of concern to the social conscience of Europe and America. We have become increasingly unwilling to accept the effects of famine, war, and catastrophe, either on individuals or on groups. This discrepancy has also been aggravated by our improved methods of medical care, which make it possible to save so many children who would have perished under earlier conditions. The hygienic impersonal orphanage described by Spitz,[46] in which children eventually die, might be regarded as the analogue of the primitive situation, within which children who are markedly defective also die, in the midst of what is apparently adequate human care. A very conspicuous example of the way in which a society selectively distinguishes between the more wanted and the less wanted child is the differential survival rate of boys and girls reported for parts of India.[44] It is worth noting that the whole ethical agitation which led first to the creation of institutions for the care of abandoned children of various sorts, and then to the movement to examine the consequences of such care, can be seen first as a social ethical reaction against processes equivalent to immediate infanticide, accompanied by a willingness to accept a very high infant death rate, and, secondly, as a social reaction against the recognition that such children, instead of dying, young and innocent, lived on as traumatized and antisocial individuals to create new social problems.

This question of dealing with the unwanted child should in turn be distinguished from the set of institutional practices which have grown up to deal with the sick child, or the child in an isolated nuclear family where power to care for the child has been impaired by illness or death. Here the urgency towards reform is provided by the mother who learns what the isolation of the infant at birth, or the separation imposed on husband and siblings, or the isolation of a sick child in the hospital, may do to a very loved and valued child. Where the Spitz [47] and Appell & Aubry [1] films were shown to the same group, followed by the Robertson film, " A Two-Year-Old Goes to Hospital ",[42] the contrast in responses to the films was very great : the Spitz and Appell & Aubry films were rejected, in line with the original rejection of the children, while the Robertson film was reacted to as something that " might have happened to any of our own children ".

Although much of the same reasoning is applied to the revision of maternity hospitals and children's wards as is also applied to the reform of institutions for the care of the unwanted child, the very real differences involved in the impersonal and professional implementation of an impersonal ethic — no child should be allowed to die or have its personality deformed — and the personal ethic — my child, or our child, must be protected — should never be lost sight of.

DIFFERENCES IN SURVIVAL CONDITIONS

A second set of differences between studies in modern large societies and those in primitive societies lies in the actual conditions of survival. Under primitive conditions the infant is entirely dependent upon breast milk, whether from its own mother alone or from a number of women, and also, in the absence of medical care, its life is exceedingly precarious. As a result, there is usually a very high death rate, and all studies of primitive methods of maternal care and their concomitants in cultural character deal only with those individuals who have been so placed, in terms of their own constitution, familial and tribal constellation and cultural practice, as to be able to survive. In no discussion of the kind of cultural character that is produced by keeping the infant close to the mother, by an available set of alternative wet nurses, by sudden and abrupt weaning, etc., are we dealing with the effects of such methods of child-rearing on the total group of infants who are born, but only upon a very small percentage who survive. The statement that every primitive mother breast-feeds her baby — and in many tribes this feeding may be interrupted by illness and resumed after weeks — is not a statement that *every* primitive mother breast-feeds *every* baby adequately. It is simply a statement that all babies who survive are breast-fed, and all women who survive child-bearing have a capacity to produce some breast milk. Where as many as five out of ten children born may die, the selectivity for certain characteristics can be very high.[39]

Two totally unjustified extrapolations from the conditions where all infants were breast-fed were made during the discussions of breast-feeding — and mother and child separation — of the 1940's. It was assumed that because in such situations all surviving babies were breast-fed, breast-feeding could be advised for all infants. And it was assumed that because all parturient women had some milk, this milk could be assumed to be capable — if only the proper psychological attitude and medical support were there — of nourishing the newborn.[28] Both assumptions were naïve extrapolations which failed to take into account the differences between societies where most infants die and there are no artificial feeding methods available, and societies where most infants live and artificial feeding methods are available. A careful comparison of these very different conditions leads to the conclusion that failure to produce milk to nourish an infant which is demonstrating its non-viability by failing to thrive on the breast milk its mother gives it is a biologically adequate response on the part of the primitive mother. The cycle — failure of the child to gain weight, failure of breast milk, increased failure of the child, mediated by the mother's perception of the situation, maternal anxiety — whether an example of maternal rejection or not, is biologically appropriate behaviour. The modern mother whose milk does not agree with her child is behaving with biological appropriateness when she responds with anxiety, and then uses the culturally available means to save her child, thus correcting for a type of behaviour developed through many thousands and possibly hundreds of thousands of years. The mother who stubbornly insists on attempting to breast-feed a child who does not thrive, and the physician who attributes the failure of the particular physicochemical biological combination of that mother and child to " maternal rejection " or even to " infantile rejection " is failing to take these factors into account.[33]

Having separated out the types of evidence available from primitive cultures, the particular extension of the question of the unwanted child in the institutions of the modern world (orphanages), the confusion between institutional practices which interrupt the continuity of person-to-person relationships for the unwanted child and for the wanted child temporarily hospitalized, and the confusions introduced by applying the " success " of breast-feeding at a primitive level to a modern level, we may now tackle the series of questions raised earlier in this chapter.

REMOVAL OF CHILDREN TO IMPERSONAL INSTITUTIONS

We may first consider the removal of children from the care of familiar people to impersonal institutions where they are cared for impersonally. Here all the evidence must come from the study of such institutions, and the only addition that anthropological studies can make is the insistence that institutions in several different cultures must be scrutinized by the same methods and with equal care, taking all the socio-cultural factors into account, before we can be certain that the low survival rate is due to the lack of interpersonal continuity. Differences in nutrition and sanitation, in religious beliefs and in cultural valuation of boys and girls, the sources from which the institutionalized children are drawn, the nature of the personnel who care for the children, the involvement or non-involvement of the mothers of illegitimate children, the belief within the institution about the desirability of institutionalization *versus* adoption, whether the infants enter at birth or later — all these are factors which need to be examined before it is possible to make scientifically valid statements about the ability of the human infant to live without strong, continuing interpersonal ties. The evidence that has been gathered so far is quite strong enough to suggest that this is a hazardous method of attempting to care for infants and children, and one which no authority is justified in risking if any other means are available. The evidence is, in fact, quite strong enough to suggest that present institutional practices are only a prolonged, ritualized method of disposing of the infant for whom no one wishes to care. But the evidence is not complete enough to show that with a will to give such institutionalized infants the same level of attention and care as that given by individual parents, the survival rate under institutional care might not be as high or higher. The weight of evidence from the *Kibbutzim*, where group care for loved children, not unwanted, anonymous children, is practised, suggest that, whatever the other by-products in later character structure, group care with high degrees of discontinuity provides for survival under institutionalized conditions.[45] The lethal element in orphanages may be the cultural acceptance of the " unwanted " state of the infant, rather than any specific way in which this unwantedness is mediated to an infant. Similarly, a mother who knows her child is going to die will, as the child gradually fades away, mediate to it the knowledge of its approaching death.

The untoward effects of hospitalization, or temporary separation of wanted children from familiar adults, can then be interpreted as the condition within which the hospital set-up, rules about visiting, and anxieties of the parents themselves mediate to the young child a sense of break with the familiar tie, with consequent separation anxiety. Here again the data are sufficient to alert the medical world to the dangers involved, but are not sufficient to prove that this sense of break is unavoidable if the mother does not accompany the child; although often it cannot be prevented as easily in the absence of the mother, it can be prevented.

Here again the traditional mother-child tie based on breast-feeding is, of course, the easiest method to assure a child continuity of relationship — if we are willing to disregard the extent to which the mother's biologically adequate anxiety may also endanger the child's life, not only by a biologically adequate failure in breast milk, but also by mediating to the child her biological knowledge of how ill and vulnerable it is.

SUPPLEMENTING BIOLOGICAL PARENTAL BEHAVIOUR

We may go on, in fact, to consider whether the discoveries which have transformed the capacity which we share with other mammals to accept or reject our young into a capacity to preserve the lives of an increasing number of human infants may not actually be discoveries of ways of overcoming the handicaps of the biologically given aspects of maternity. Biological mothering is heavily susceptible to conditions of pregnancy, whether the child was wanted or unwanted, its sex, the conditions of the mother's own childhood, relationships to the father, the nature of the delivery and the nature of the postnatal contact between mother and child, and finally the fit between the structure and functioning of the mother's breast and the infant's constitution.[13] The cultural invention — in contrast to the simple biological one — is that of conscious nurturing. Biological motherhood is a routine occurrence in the natural world; nursing — the responsible, devoted, conscious care of the young — is cultural and human. We ought perhaps to be discussing not how much should a nurse be like a mother, but how much can a mother be like a good nurse.

The shift from the practice of burying the infant alive if its mother dies to that of the shared breast-feeding of other women was the beginning of this order of nurturing, continued in various forms of artificial feeding, until men, as well as women, could share in the cultural nurturing of an infant.

So when we consider the effects of separation, the question may well be asked: What are the consequences of separating the infant, or child, from that person, or persons, who have given it good *nursing* care ? The existence of a biological tie may be not only irrelevant but actually lethal.

THE NEONATAL PERIOD

It is generally recognized that the biological specificity of mother-child ties, and even father-child ties — inasmuch as expectant fathers often have certain biochemical responses during their wives' pregnancies[36] — may be expected to be closest during pregnancy, delivery and the immediate neonatal period, and that culturally diversified conditions may be expected to exert more and more influence the greater the distance from birth. It might be expected that under "primitive conditions" there would be found a greater correspondence between culturally patterned care and biologically given "instinctive behaviour" than in our more artificial modern cultures. Actually, with the exception of the dependence upon breast milk and such "natural" conditions as arise from ignorance of modern obstetrical methods, we find in primitive societies a great deal of "artificial" or culturally regulated behaviour surrounding gestation, delivery, and postnatal care. Although a case can be made for the biological basis of any frequently occurring phenomenon, such as morning sickness, maternal cravings, and transfer to the father of a series of imputed attitudes of illness, fatigue, and debility, there are many other societies, equally primitive, in which these biological possibilities have not been institutionalized. Furthermore, the mother may be required to do everything for herself — cut the cord and bathe the baby — or everything may be done for her; the father may be required to be present or rigorously banished; attendance at the birth may be limited to close relatives or to women who have borne children, or birth may take place in the midst of a chattering crowd. The infant may be placed at the mother's dry breast, fed at once by another woman, kept without food until the mother has milk, or may not be allowed to feed from its mother's breast until "true milk" has appeared. The infant may be kept completely covered up, protected from light and all but a minimum of air; it may be held constantly by its mother or by some other woman, or hung in a basket, or strapped to a cradle board.[25] In short, the accumulated evidence from primitive societies suggests that at a very early stage in human history, traditional modes of behaviour were evolved which were related not to any immediate instinctive pattern of neonatal mother-child relationship — such as has been described, for example, for goats and sheep and reindeer and moose — but rather to other parts of the learned behaviour of the particular people, their mode of life, means of transport, type of shelter, system of kinship organization, methods of economic exchange, and beliefs about the soul and the cosmos. Within these extremely diverse systems, in those tribes which have themselves survived, enough infants have survived to perpetuate their cultures to the point of record. However, there are instances in which small human groups have not developed a culture which had sufficient resistance to the impact of a foreign culture to continue to reproduce themselves under conditions of change. The failure appears to come in fertility — in instances such as that of the Marquesas, where, during a nine-month stay of three anthropologists from September 1920 to June 1921, according to the report of one of the anthropologists, no child was born in any locality where he was staying,[14] in islands where the population had once been numbered up to 100 000, and possibly slightly more.[43, 49] But with the type of field work that was being done, with an emphasis on material culture and on gross features of the social organization, it might not have been realized that miscarriages and still births — and even live births given no encouragement to live — could have been responsible for the population fall.[18, 48] Against such reports, we have to place the records of more recent times, which demonstrate that under conditions of extreme starvation of the mother, the gestating infant has survived, only to show the effect of the starvation later in failure to mature or to reproduce.[38]

Primitive materials, therefore, give no support to the theory that there is a " natural " connexion between conditions of human gestation and delivery and appropriate cultural practices. The tie between the mother and child can be established by delivery practices which enjoin Spartan behaviour, which permit the mother to writhe and scream, or which combine the agonies of a prolonged birth with accusations of infidelity or sin. The tie between a man and his wife's child can be established by any number of arrangements: he may not see the child for a month after it is born;[22] it may be attributed to him because he, among his brothers, several of whom share the same wife, performed the paternity-acknowledging ritual years ago and no other brother has performed it;[41] he may claim it when it is born three months after he has returned from a year's absence, on the theory that it " hurried up to see its father's face ";[25] or, in modern rather than primitive terms, after agreeing to artificial insemination, the mother's husband may insist "he really looks like me".* Thus, fatherhood is a cultural construct based upon a man's relationship to the children borne by a woman with whom he has had sex relations.

We may thus say that the establishment of permanent nurturing ties both between a woman and the child she bears, and between a man and the child borne by a woman with whom he has had sex relationships, is dependent upon cultural patterning in which the ideas about what constitutes motherhood and fatherhood, and later sibling relations, are of overriding importance. Among some primitive peoples, habits of

---

* Unpublished studies of attitudes of husbands of women who have received artificial insemination

adoption before birth accentuate this dependence upon cultural arrangements, so that the adoptive parents take over the infant at birth, even to the point of the dry-breasted adoptive mother inducing milk in her own breast with which to feed the adoptive child.[23] In parts of the Middle East it is the milk tie which establishes a woman's relationship to a child, her own or a foster-child; gestation is not regarded as establishing the relationship between mother and child.[12]

PATTERNING OF CHARACTER FORMATION

Such evidence does not suggest, however, that the patterns of relationship and the theory of how they originated and how they should affect the future life of the infant may not be significantly related to the kind of child care, the kind of parenthood, and the kind of character structure which is found in a given society. If all children are expected to live and every effort is made to keep the puny and the defective alive, this changes the position of all individuals in a given society. If the father is allowed, or required, to care for the young infant, a tie is established which is absent when such behaviour is not customary. Whether the mother's right to keep her child is dependent upon the decisions of her relatives, or upon those of her husband, or if she herself is given the cultural right to decide whether the child should live or die, this will also change the quality of parenthood, and the culturally determined character structure. But whether a biological parent does or does not provide the best care for a child is, in all known cultures, a function of how biological parenthood is phrased, not of the establishment of point-for-point " natural " — i.e., pre-human — conditions of delivery and child-rearing.

THE ASSUMED NEED FOR A SINGLE MOTHER-FIGURE

The Bowlby findings are not, however, primarily concerned with these early hours of birth, nor with the presence or absence of the " biological mother ", but rather with an imputed need, in human infants, for a mothering-figure during the first years of life. The assumption is that there is a biologically given need for continuity in this mother-child relationship, that it is a pair relationship which cannot be safely distributed among several figures, and that all attempts to diffuse or divide it and all interruptions are necessarily harmful in character, emotionally damaging, if not completely lethal. Although, logically, continuous care by a foster-mother or nurse meets the Bowlby requirements as well as such care by the biological mother, there is a demand that this continuity be accorded to, and provided by, the biological mother — a demand which is based on a mixed and unexamined set of premises.

It might be claimed that the biological mother establishes a shared tie with her newborn infant owing to the establishment during and after birth of a series of biologically given responses, to the infant's cry, to the smell of the mother's body, to the shape of the mother's nipple, to the nature of the infant's sucking reflex, that is of such an order that it will assure the kind of continuity of later care that the infant requires. This argument would then read: infants need the continuous presence of a mothering-figure and Nature has provided a set of mechanisms which if permitted full play will establish just these conditions. Other methods of establishing such a pair relationship are less reliable — especially under modern urban conditions, which are implicitly assumed throughout the Bowlby analysis. If this shared tie is to include breast-feeding, without supplementary feeding, which is the surest method of making the mother and child — the nursing couple [35] — into an exclusive pair relationship, then, as has been discussed above, only a limited number of infants will thrive and survive. An actual return, on the part of society, to such a demand would result in a tremendously increased infant death rate, a change in our medical values — where life is a value at all costs — and might, if widely enough propagated, present some answer to the population explosion.

Actually, such an exclusive and continuous relationship between mother and infant is only possible under highly artificial urban conditions, which combine the production of food outside the home and the practice of contraception. For under primitive conditions there are two situations which require a break in the continuity of mother-child care: (a) the need of the other children for care, and (b) the demands on the mother for food gathering, materials gathering, horticultural and other contributions to the food supply of the family group. The assumption that a mother-child pair relationship can be maintained without interruption until the child is two actually exposes the child to more traumata than if it is expected that several women can breast-feed and care for the child, that a young girl or a grandmother or even a father can give it a dry breast for comfort, and that supplementary — premasticated — food can be made available to it at any time. It is among those people who consider that only the mother can care for the child that the child must be taken to the fields — and may be carried off by wolves, as in parts of India [19] — or left hungry and miserable in the village, as in Alor, bereft because there is no mother-substitute, while the mother is away at work in the gardens. Studies of the character structure of the members of tribes among whom such exclusive relationships obtain — notably the Alorese [9] and the Dobuans [11] — as compared with that of the Samoans, support Bowlby's position that separation from an exclusive mother-figure has a negative effect on character, but also suggest that diffusion of breast-feeding, feeding and nurturing ties among a number of females of all ages, as in the typical Samoan large household, ensures the child greater continuity of human care and less liability to trauma. It is significant that the Samoans, who are conspicuous in the extent to which mother-child ties are diffused, also have one of the highest birth rates in the world.*

The question may still be raised, as it has been by Konrad Lorenz,[50] whether the cultivation of more exclusive and more intense parent-child relationships is not a pre-condition of the kind of character structure which is necessary to maintain and develop our kind of civilization. Here the argument would centre, not on whether life is more precarious for a child dependent only upon its biological mother for care, but rather on whether individuals so reared do not show a different and more desirable — in terms of the stated requirements of the modern world — character structure. The most definitive materials available, aside from the studies of primitive societies, are those collected by Spiro on children of the *Kibbutzim* system in Israel.[45] Although the single *Kibbutz* which Spiro studied is too small to be definitive, the analysis which he presents is persuasive. Children reared with age-peers, with changing and over-burdened nurses, who see parents, themselves reared in old-style small families, for short intervals every day, combine excessive responsiveness to parental behaviour with excessive dependence upon the peer group, and in youth become heavily dependent upon the members of the peer group with whom they were reared. The Hutterite studies,[10] in which the parents were reared within the same system as the children, with children isolated for most of the time from association with their own parents, confirm the extent to which children so reared are dependent upon the community and unfitted for venturing forth as individuals. Neither of these bodies of data suggests that children do not thrive and survive under conditions of group nurturing; they both suggest, however, that their mobility and flexibility are impaired.

Data on children within the extended family systems of China [7,8] and India,[20,21] which involve multiple nurturing figures, ranging from child nurses to the aged, would seem to confirm the impression from the primitive materials that there is security in a larger number of nurturing figures, and that rearing in such a setting leads to fecundity. The question may still be raised as to the character structure of individuals so reared, as Kenneth Soddy has done,[17] but incomplete data on Chinese character structure suggest a range of subtlety and flexibility of personality far beyond that of Westerners, although less complex than that of the

---

* 38.0 $^0/_{00}$ for Western Samoa (1958), 39.4 $^0/_{00}$ for American Samoa (1959); as compared with 24.1 $^0/_{00}$ for the USA (1959), rates beneath 20.0 $^0/_{00}$ for the European countries and an estimate for rural India of 39 $^0/_{00}$ (data obtained from the United Nations Statistical Office).

Japanese, among whom the child-rearing pattern involves discontinuity of style — early indulgence followed by rigorous discipline — rather than discontinuity of persons.[3,4]

TASKS OF MODERN HEALTH AGENCIES

The evidence suggests that those agencies that are charged with the development of international standards of human care compatible with existing international aspirations have, in the case of problems of maternal separation and deprivation, two quite distinct tasks: (*a*) the development of standards for institutional treatment of children, in orphanages, hospitals, day-care centres, crèches, or kindergartens, etc., in which findings on comparable institutions already exist but need to be reinterpreted for each culture and each set of local conditions; and (*b*) the further investigation of different types of family structure within different cultural settings, and the implications of different types of child care for the development of cultural character, both in the children who receive it and in the parents who carry it out. There is undoubtedly evidence enough to warrant the advocacy of such public measures as aid to dependent children, provision of day care rather than residential care for the children of working mothers, hospitalization where continuity with home figures, not necessarily the mother, unless she has had the sole care of the child, is possible, extreme caution in changes of foster-home, and precautions for the care of children from homes that are broken by divorce and death. The problem remains, however, of how to separate the necessary protection of a child who has been isolated in an exclusive pair relationship with the mother — of a type which cannot be said to be natural at a human level, because it actually does not permit participation by the father, care of the dependent older siblings, and ties with the three-generation family, all of which are human experiences — from advocacy of the artificial perpetuation, intensification or creation of such conditions of exclusive mother-child dependence.

The effects of Bowlby's original monograph were highly beneficial to the degree that world-wide attention was focused on the evils of impersonal institutional care for infants and young children and on types of hospitalization of either mother or child which resulted in traumatic interruptions of a highly exclusive relationship. These effects have been partially nullified, however, by the reification into a set of universals of a set of ethnocentric observations on our own society, combined with assumptions of biological requirements which are incompatible with *Homo sapiens*, although possibly compatible with an earlier stage when a two-year-old could fend for himself, and the family did not exist.

One further remark may be made. Preparation for change — radical, rapid change — is the greatest single educational requirement in the world today.[26,27,31,32] It is possible that the re-establishment of early mother-child relationships that have been ignored throughout the existence of human culture might be a social invention of great importance. Just as the ability to self-select food has been practically unexploited throughout the life of living things, but can be observed today when rats are permitted to choose among synthetic vitamins,[40] so also there may be human potentialities which date far back in evolutionary times, for which new artificially created conditions may find a new use. Exposure of young fathers in the USA to unusual contact with young infants has been accompanied by a far greater and, in some cases, extreme interest in infants, and a diversion of young males from the more customary fields of public extra-domestic activity. The human infant is capable at birth of moving over a flat surface for a considerable distance. This is a potentiality that has not been used in any known society; instead the adult hand manipulates the child. But the use of this early capability might lay the basis for a different kind of kinaesthetic awareness which might be useful to man, for example, in adapting to different types of gravitational field — in space flight or space colonization.

If the invocation of the great variety of latent biological potentials is recognized, not as a return to the natural, but as a new use of man's potential, as human society evolves and incorporates an increasing awareness of our own nature, it should be possible to develop ways of child-rearing which allow for individual differences, among infants, among mothers, and in the pairing of each infant and mother, which would not restore a previous state of precarious well-being — which depended on a high infant death rate and a relatively slowly changing culture — but which would establish a new level of human existence.

REFERENCES

1. Appell, G. & Aubry, J. (1951) *Maternal deprivation in young children* (Film: 16 mm; 22 min.; sound. Distributors: New York University Film Library; Tavistock Child Development Research Unit, London; United Nations, Geneva). [For discussion of film, see: Aubry, J. (1955) *The case of Monique*. In: Soddy, K., ed., *Mental health and infant development*, London, Routledge & Kegan Paul, Vol. 1, p. 125]

2. Bateson, G. & Mead, M. (1952) *Karba's first years* (Film: 16 mm; 19 min.; sound. Distributor: New York University Film Library) [Films on Character Formation in Different Cultures]

3. Benedict, R. (1946) *The chrysanthemum and the sword*, Boston, Houghton Mifflin

4. Benedict, R. (1949) Child rearing in certain European countries. *Amer. J. Orthopsychiat.*, **19**, 342

5. Bowlby, J. (1952) *Maternal care and mental health*, 2nd ed., Geneva (*World Health Organization: Monograph Series*, No. 2)

6. Bruch, H. (1952) *Don't be afraid of your child*, New York, Farrar, Strauss & Young

7. Bunzel, R. (1950) *Explorations in Chinese culture*, New York (Columbia University Research in Contemporary Cultures) [Unpublished report filed with the Institute for Intercultural Studies, Inc., New York]

8. Chiang Yee (1940) *A Chinese childhood*, London, Methuen

9. Dubois, C. (1944) *The people of Alor*, Minneapolis, University of Minnesota Press

10. Eaton, J. W. & Weil, R. J. (1955) *Culture and mental disorders*, Glencoe, Ill., The Free Press

11. Fortune, R. F. (1932) *Sorcerers of Dobu*, London, Routledge & Kegan Paul

12. Granqvist, H. (1947) *Birth and childhood among the Arabs: studies in a Muhammadan village in Palestine*, Helsingfors, Soderstron

13. Gunther, M. (1955) Instinct and the nursing couple. *Lancet*, **1**, 575

14. Handy, E. S. C. (1923) The native culture in the Marquesas. *B. P. Bishop Mus. Bull (Honolulu)*, No. 9, p. 72

15. Kluckhohn, C. & Leighton, D. C. (1946) *The Navaho*, Cambridge, Mass., Harvard University Press

16. Leighton, A. H. & Leighton, D. L. (1949) The Ramah project. In: Gregorio the hand-trembler. *Pap. Peabody Mus. Archaeol. Ethnol. (Cambridge, Mass.)*, **40**, No. 1, p.v

17. Lin, Tsung-Yi (1960) *Reality and vision: a report of the First Asian Seminar on Mental Health and Family Life, Baguio, Philippines, 6-20 December 1958, sponsored jointly by the Government of the Republic of the Philippines, the Asia Foundation, the World Federation for Mental Health, the World Health Organization*, Manila

18. Maher, R. F. (1961) *New men of Papua*, Madison, University of Wisconsin Press

19. Mandelbaum, D. G. (1943) Wolf-child histories from India, *J. soc. Psychol.*, **17**, 25

20. Mandelbaum, D. G. (1959) *The family in India.* In: Anshen, R.N., ed., *The family: its function and destiny*, New York, Harper, p. 167

21. Mayer, A. C. (1960) *Caste and kinship in central India*, Berkeley, University of California Press, p. 214

22. Mead, M. (1930) *Growing up in New Guinea*, New York, Morrow

23. Mead, M. (1935) *Sex and temperament in three primitive societies*, New York, Morrow, Part II

24. Mead, M. (1939) Researches in Bali, 1936-39. *Trans. N. Y. Acad. Sci., Ser. 2*, **2**, 24

25. Mead, M. (1949) *Male and female*, New York, Morrow

26. Mead, M. (1951) *The school in American culture (the Inglis Lecture, 1950)*, Cambridge, Mass., Harvard University Press

27. Mead, M., ed. (1953) *Cultural patterns and technical change*, Paris, UNESCO

28. Mead, M. (1954) Some theoretical considerations on the problem of mother-child separation. *Amer. J. Orthopsychiat.*, **24**, 471

29. Mead, M. (1954) The swaddling hypothesis; its reception. *Amer. Anthropol.*, **56**, 395

30. Mead, M. (1954) *Research on primitive children*. In: Carmichael, L., ed., *Manual of child psychology*, 2nd ed., New York, Wiley, p. 735

31. Mead, M. (1954) Cultural discontinuities and personality transformation. *J. soc. Issues* (Suppl. Series No. 8, Kurt Lewin Memorial Award Issue)

32. Mead, M. (1956) *New lives for old*, New York, Morrow

33. Mead, M. (1957) Changing patterns of parent-child relations in an urban culture. *Int. J. Psycho-Anal.*, **38**, 1

34. Mead, M. & Macgregor, F. C. (1951) *Growth and culture*, New York, Putnam

35. Middlemore, M. P. (1941) *The nursing couple*, London, Hamish Hamilton

36. Mirsky, I. A. (1950) Pepsinogen excretion (uropepsin) as an index of the influence of various life situations on gastric secretion. *Ass. Res. nerv. Dis. Proc.*, **29**, 628

37. Orlansky, H. (1949) Infant care and personality. *Psychol. Bull.*, **46**, 1

38. Peller, S. (1940) Growth, heredity and environment. *Growth*, **4**, 277

39. *Report of a conference organized by the World Federation for Mental Health on malnutrition and food habits, held in Cuernavaca, Mexico, September 9-14, 1960* [editor: A. Burgess] (in press)

40. Richter, C. P. (1943) *The self-selection of diets*. In: *Essays in biology, in honour of Herbert M. Evans*, Berkeley, University of California Press, p. 499

41. Rivers, W. H. R. (1906) *The Todas*, London, Macmillan

42. Robertson, J. (1952) *A two-year-old goes to hospital* (Film: 16 mm; 45 min.; sound. Distributors: Tavistock Child Development Research Unit, London; New York University Film Library; United Nations, Geneva)
[For discussion of film, see: Bowlby, J. & Robertson, J. (1955) *A two-year-old goes to hospital*. In: Soddy, K., ed., *Mental health and infant development*, London, Routledge & Kegan Paul, Vol. 1, p. 123]

43. Shapiro, H. L. (1958) Les îles Marquises. *Nat. History*, **67**, 208

44. Soddy, K., ed. (1961) *Cross-cultural studies in mental health: Identity-mental health and value systems*, London, Tavistock Publications

45. Spiro, M. (1958) *Children of the Kibbutz*, Cambridge, Mass., Harvard University Press

46. Spitz, R. (1945) *Hospitalism*. In: *The psychoanalytic study of the child*, New York, International Universities Press, Vol. 1, p. 53

47. Spitz, R. *Grief, a peril in infancy; The smiling response* (Films: 16 mm; 30 min., 20 min.; Silent. Distributor: New York University Film Library)
[For discussion of films, see: Spitz, R. (1955) *The influence of the mother-child relationship and its disturbance* and *The case of Felicia*. In: Soddy, K., ed.,

Mental health and infant development, London, Routledge & Kegan Paul, Vol. 1, pp. 103, 109]

48. Strecker, R. L. & Emlen, J. J., jr (1953) Regulatory mechanisms in house-mouse populations; the effect of limited food supply. *Ecology*, **34**, 375

49. Suggs, R. *Marquesan sexual behavior* (in preparation)

50. Tanner, J. M. & Inhelder, B., ed. (1956) *Discussions on child development*, London Tavistock Publications, Vol. 2 [Proceedings of the Second Meeting of the WHO Study Group on the Psychobiological Development of the Child, London, 1954]

A SOCIAL SCIENTIST'S APPROACH
TO MATERNAL DEPRIVATION

BARBARA WOOTTON [*]

Since publication of my *Social Science and Social Pathology* [23] I have not undertaken substantial further research into theories of the effects of maternal separation or deprivation. Most of the later studies that have come to my notice do not appear to have advanced the argument very significantly either in one direction or in the other. Many of them deal only with very small samples, or concentrate upon the experience of children who have been hospitalized, which for reasons given later in this chapter is not a very good basis for generalizations regarding the effects of maternal separation as such. Criticisms of Bowlby's handling of the evidence in his follow-up study [7] have been made in a correspondence in the *Lancet*, [12, 22] but neither these nor Dr Bowlby's reply [5] take us very far. Hence, although I have added references to a few studies of major importance which were not available at the time that my book went to press, this chapter is in the main an abbreviated reproduction of what I have already said in the relevant chapter of that book. [**]

The maternal deprivation theories propounded by Dr Bowlby in his monograph [4] seem to have been criticized on several distinct grounds. First it is said that Dr Bowlby in his comparisons between separated and non-separated children paid too little attention to the findings of studies which run counter to his theory as to the damaging effects of separation. He mentions in fact only three of these — namely, Orgel's study of only 16 children, Brown's comparison of 200 children from orphanages and 100 boys of low socio-economic status with a group of 200 children drawn at random from the general population, and the study made by Bodman and others of 51 institutionalized children with 52 brought up in their own homes. On these Bowlby comments, not unfairly, that " none of them is of high scientific quality ".

Too much must not, I think, be made of this particular criticism — for the reason that, at the time that Bowlby wrote his monograph,

[*] House of Lords, England.
[**] For permission to reprint this, I am much indebted to the generosity of my publishers, Messrs George Allen & Unwin Ltd.

little serious evidence could be found against the hypothesis that institutionalized children tend to be backward in development. In fact if the
hypothesis is stated in these terms (a point on which more will be said
presently) the weight of evidence is clearly on Bowlby's side, at least
up to the date of his monograph; though, as Bowlby has himself since
acknowledged, some of the authors upon whose work he relied, such as
Bender, Goldfarb and Spitz, did on occasion overstate their case.

Since that date, however, fresh doubts have been raised by further
studies — notably in England by Dr Hilda Lewis's study of 500 children
admitted to a reception centre. Lewis found that

" Unless separation of child from mother had occurred before the age of two
years and had been lasting, it bore no statistically significant relation to the
normality or otherwise of the child's mental state at the time of admission. No clear
connexion was evident between separation from the mother and a particular pattern
of disturbed behaviour. Neither delinquency nor incapacity for affectionate relationships was significantly more frequent in the separated children ".[15]

It was, moreover, the mildly, rather than the violently, disturbed
children who accounted for the statistical significance even of lasting
separation from the mother; whereas according to the Bowlby hypothesis
" the cases of most serious harm should be found among those children
who had been separated from their mothers for long periods or permanently before the age of two years ".[15] As judged by the criteria
used by Lewis, at any rate, early or lasting separation appears to
have had no such disastrous consequences as are predicted by the
Bowlby school — an observation which does not surprise its author
in view of the fact that the mere physical presence or absence of the
child's own mother is no true index of the quality of mothering which
the child may have enjoyed. " Unduly dogmatic statements about ill-
effects of maternal deprivation ", she comments, " often leave out of
account the emotional hazards and harms children may suffer from bad
mothers and indifferent mother-substitutes, or the variety of sources
(including the father) from whom children may draw the love and support necessary for their happiness ".[15] Although separation from the
mother before the age of five years was found to be " a prognostically
adverse feature ", yet " nearly a third of the children who were
separated from their mothers [were] in a satisfactory condition at the
end of the follow-up period " (i.e., from two to three and a half years
after admission to the centre); " and permanent separation before the
age of two had not been the prelude to a particularly unsatisfactory condition of the child at the end of the period ".[15]

Inconclusive results have also been obtained both by Rowntree and
by Douglas & Blomfield. Rowntree,[19] whose study related to a sample
of the children born in Great Britain in a single week during 1946,

found that by the time they were four years old, 6% of the (legitimate) babies in the original sample were living in households in which one parent was no longer present, being dead, divorced, estranged or temporarily absent. After matching each child so deprived with another from " a stable and united family " for sex, birth order and certain family circumstances, she arrived at a total of 277 pairs for whom " complete information on social background, child health and development " was available. In the upshot the children of broken homes " were not exceptionally prone to the grosser forms of emotional disturbance, apart from a rather higher incidence of bed-wetting at four years old, which affected only the better-off families. " So far as could be estimated, " the great majority of children in broken homes were as well and as normal in behaviour as those living in more stable circumstances. " Similarly Douglas & Blomfield [8] in a survey of 4668 legitimate children found that 52% had been separated between birth and the age of six. Those separated for more than four weeks were matched with others not separated in similar types of family and the same locality. From observation of these children the authors concluded that separation did not affect children " adversely in any way if they remained at home. Among the children sent away from home, more nightmares and bad habits, such as thumb-sucking," were reported for the separated as against the controls. " Rather more of the former also attended Child Guidance and Speech Therapy clinics later. But these differences were relatively small ".[8] But the authors add this cautious comment " Although so far we have no records of serious disturbances, and most of the mothers themselves do not appear to be worried, we do not in any way regard this as a final conclusion ".[8]

Doubtless further evidence will accumulate in the course of time. In the meantime it must be accepted that the number of institutionalized children who show signs of seriously retarded development is sufficiently large to be disquieting.

A second and more serious criticism relates to the interpretation which is put upon the available evidence. Most of this is derived from crude contrasts between children living in various types of institution and those brought up in their own homes. On this basis theories have been developed in which all the emphasis is laid upon the separation experience itself, without adequate regard to the conditions that a child comes from or goes to. Indeed so obsessed are some investigators with the importance of the separation experience and so convinced that its roots are as much biological as social that they think it worth while to make experiments as to the effects of maternal separation on young animals. In consequence they have been remarkably blind to the dangers of relying upon evidence from institutions, and, in particular, to the variables introduced by the use of arbitrarily selected institutions. In order to establish that the damaging factor in a child's experience is his separation from home rather than the régime of the particular institution in which he finds himself, it would be necessary to study the development, not only of a sufficient sample of children, but also of children who have lived in a sufficiently representative sample of institutions. An institution is not a standard unit; and there can be good institutions as well as bad ones. Generally speaking the information given by investigators (notably Goldfarb, Spitz, Roudinesco) about the way in which their institutionalized children lived is far from full. One is, however, left with the impression that these children were not as a rule very intelligently or even always very kindly treated. Nor has sufficient weight generally been given to the possibility that communal homes for children may differ from families in other respects beside the opportunity which they offer for intimate affectionate relationships. How, one would like to know, were the institutionalized children fed? Could their backwardness have been due, in any degree, to dietary deficiencies? Little seems to have been done to control such important variables as these; but it is perhaps significant that a Dutch investigation,[14] covering 38 children's homes, some eight or ten years ago found much to be desired in the diet provided. Again, in many cases evidence was drawn from children who had spent considerable periods in hospital. But a hospital is a frightening place (and the illness which gets you there can be a frightening experience too), quite apart from the fact that being in hospital means being away from home and mother. Stott,[20] for instance, in an inquiry into the history of 141 backward children of whom 25 had been separated for at least 10 weeks in the first four years of life came to the conclusion that " in itself the separation certainly does not have the dire consequences that have been supposed "; and he suggests that " the early illnesses more than the separations were responsible for the later unforthcomingness and anxious over-attachment to the mother ". Sweeping condemnations of institutional life in general cannot fairly be based upon the anxieties and depression manifested by children in hospitals — even if, as some investigators have shown, sick children cheer up considerably when they are allowed to keep contact with their mothers.

What these studies of institutionalized children have revealed is not so much that children need dependable love — a truth which surely man has known in theory as long as he has ignored it in practice — as that, as things are, they are more likely to find this in families than in institutions. This, however, is a social, rather than a psychological, fact; it is a commentary upon the way in which many institutions are, or have been, run. By calling attention to the imperfections of many existing children's institutions, the separationists have undoubtedly rendered a valuable social service; but this does not alter the fact that so far as their own researches are concerned, the inferences which they have drawn are misleading and the emphasis is misplaced. When Elizabeth Fry exposed the insanitary conditions that obtained in 19th century prisons, no one applauded her for the discovery that good sanitary conditions were to be desired: the merit of her work was its demonstration that such conditions were not to be found in prisons. The parallel holds. By a curious misplacement of emphasis, even the best work on maternal deprivation seems to have obscured its own genuine discoveries by highlighting what are little more than platitudes; with the unfortunate result, as Edelston has put it, of " 'mother separation' becoming an all-embracing cliché every bit as much as the 'broken home' ".[9] In this connexion it is indeed pertinent to recall both Margaret Mead's observation that " cross-cultural studies suggest that adjustment is most facilitated if the child is cared for by many warm, friendly people ",[16] and her plea to the WHO Study Group on the Psychobiological Development of the Child in 1954 that we should restyle our lives so that children can learn that there is more than one person whom they can trust.[21]

Uncritical reliance upon the experience of institutions has resulted further in the separation theorists paying too little attention to the background of the children concerned. Institutionalized children are not a random sample of the population of their age. Factors that may well be important have too often been neglected; and even where these have been recognized, they have in some cases been treated with a levity that is altogether astonishing. Thus Bowlby, commenting in his monograph on a comparative study by Theis, observes that " so far as could be determined the heredity of the two groups was similar... Since heredity is, so far as possible, held constant for these two groups, the difference cannot be explained in this way " (p. 40).[4] Even with the qualification " so far as could be determined ", such a light-hearted dismissal of the influence of differential inherited factors is astonishingly naïve. Again Bowlby has himself stated that the main criterion by which the presence of defective hereditary factors in his study of forty-four juvenile thieves was diagnosed was " the presence of neurosis, psychosis, or serious psychopathy in parents or grandparents " (p. 34) [4] — a criterion which implies a degree of confidence, both as to the diagnoses of two generations earlier and as to the conditions governing the inheritance of morbid mental conditions, which can hardly be justified by the evidence on the subject.

A third criticism of Dr Bowlby's theories relates to the hypothesis that the damaging effects of separation are irreversible. On this Bowlby, along with other investigators such as Aubry and Spitz, has committed himself rather far. " There is ", he wrote in his monograph, " abundant evidence that deprivation can have adverse effects on the development of children (a) during the period of separation, (b) during the period immediately after restoration to maternal care, and (c) permanently " (p. 47); [4] and from Goldfarb's work he draws the inference that even good mothering " is almost useless if delayed until after the age of 2½ years " (p. 49).[4] Actually, however, hardly any evidence is available to support such far-reaching conclusions unless indeed we are to accept as axiomatic the view that nobody's personality can change after, at latest, adolescence or early adult life. On any other assumption there can be no justification whatever for speaking of " permanent ", " irreparable " or " irreversible " damage unless and until the victims of maternal deprivation have been followed right through life. Up to now, however, few investigations have succeeded in tracing the fortunes of the maternally deprived after adolescence: instances of follow-up beyond marriage are quite exceptional. Even in the follow-up study of Beres & Obers, none of the subjects was over twenty-six, and Theis, who kept track of some of her subjects up to the age of forty, stands practically alone. Rarely, therefore, has it yet been possible to test the — on the face of it not unreasonable — possibility that the injuries of those who may have suffered from infantile deprivation might in later life be healed by a happy choice of spouse. Indeed, we can still congratulate ourselves that no evidence at all has yet been produced that comes near to justifying the depressing claim that to be sent to an institution in infancy is tantamount to being wrecked for life. Whatever the future may show, reference in the present state of knowledge to the " permanent ", " irreversible " or " irreparable " damage due to separation is reckless and unjustified.

The fourth criticism to be mentioned relates to the weight to be attached to separation experience as a factor in delinquency. It was, apparently, the study of a particular type of delinquent that first aroused Bowlby's interest in a possible connexion between maternal deprivation and antisocial behaviour. But the thieves who were the subject of this investigation, it should not be forgotten, numbered only forty-four. Out of this total seventeen were found to have suffered early or prolonged separation from their mothers or mother-figures during the first five years of their lives, as against only two of the forty-four controls who were drawn from other children attending the same child guidance clinic; while of the fourteen thieves who were specifically labelled affectionless, twelve had been separated, as against five of the remaining thirty. In this group the affectionless children were found to be " significantly more delinquent than the other thieves "; and they constituted "more than half of the more serious and chronic offenders "; [3] and, in additional support of his own conclusions, Bowlby adds that in " the late 1930's, at least six independent workers were struck by the frequency with which children who committed numerous delinquencies, who seemed to have no feelings for anyone and were very difficult to treat, were found to have had grossly disturbed relationships with their mothers in their early years " (p. 30). [4] Of these " delinquencies ", however, no evidence is given.

In addition to his own forty-four thieves, Bowlby has quoted both Burt's and the Gluecks' investigations. Yet when the subjects of the latter study were followed up, the question whether they had enjoyed " the affectionate regard of their mothers "[10] turned out to have nothing to do with the persistence of their delinquent behaviour. Clearly this finding (to which no reference is made in the Bowlby monograph) is in direct conflict with Bowlby's own conclusion that the two factors which are especially common among *persistent* delinquents, and which distinguish them from "children suffering from other forms of maladjustment", are separation for six months or more from the mother or mother-figure in the first five years, during which the child is with strangers, and " being more or less unwanted by parents who are themselves unstable and unhappy people and whose attitudes towards him are, on balance, hostile, critical and punishing. "[18]

Nor does the experience of the Hawthorne-Cedar Knolls School or Armstrong's study of runaway boys, both of which are quoted by Bowlby, add anything to the evidence of a link between separation and delinquency. For the Hawthorne-Cedar Knolls School, as Bowlby has himself stated, deals primarily with " grave psychiatric disorders "; and its population is, therefore, hardly typical of the delinquent world in general; while runaways, though sometimes delinquent, cannot be identified with those guilty of stealing or other criminal acts.

Undoubtedly the affectionless child with a life-story of unhappy experience of institutional life is one of the classical types of delinquent, and undoubtedly it is one of the most difficult types with which schools, courts and other agencies are called upon to deal. No evidence has, however, been produced to support the view that this type constitutes anything but a small minority of the delinquent population; or that, as Bowlby put it in 1946, " prolonged separation of a child from his mother (or mother-substitute) during the first five years of life stands foremost among the causes of delinquent character development and persistent misbehaviour ".[3] Later evidence has, moreover, raised fresh doubts. Thus Edelston reports that he is led by his study of the effects upon children of the " hospitalization trauma " to believe that " the proportion of delinquent reactions is not very large ".[9] Again, R. G. Andry concluded from his examination of eighty delinquents and eighty controls that " separations between a child and one or other or both parents... do not seem to be primary factors in the etiology of delinquency ";[2] and Hilda Lewis found that " Neither delinquency nor incapacity for affectionate relationships was significantly more frequent in the separated children ".[15] In the Gluecks' latest work, the evidence is also equivocal. On the one hand, this investigation produced considerable concrete detail showing that the delinquents' home and family life was generally less satisfactory than that of the controls; yet at the same time " a considerable likeness " was observed " between the delinquents and non-delinquents in respect to the time at which the physical cohesion of their families first suffered a blow. "[11] In the broken families, 56.3% of the delinquents and 46.7% of the controls were under the age of five when the break occurred; while 28.1% and 31.0%, respectively, were between five and nine years old at the time of the break. It follows that the break in the families of 84.4% of the delinquents and 77.7% of the controls occurred before the children concerned were ten years old. The differences are thus not very large. Finally we have Naess's study [17] of delinquent children in Oslo, published since the Bowlby monograph, in which she selected from the files of the Oslo Child Protection Council those cases which showed what she interpreted as a " delinquent character development " in Bowlby's sense. From those in this category who had non-delinquent brothers Naess built up a group of 42 delinquents and 42 controls, matched for age. Among these she found that separations had been less frequent among the delinquents than among the controls; and she therefore concluded that in these cases mother-separation could not be considered to " 'stand foremost among the causes ' of the delinquent character development " and that " Bowlby's unreserved generalization in regard to the problem of delinquency and adult antisociability is too wide "; though at the same time she is careful to point out that there is no contradiction between these findings and Bowlby's general proposition about mother-deprivation and character development.

The fifth criticism of the theories of Dr Bowlby and his fellow workers which seems to me to carry substantial weight relates to failure to evaluate the results obtained against the experience of the population at large. The prominence of neurotic or delinquent traits in the children investigated is to some extent explained by the fact that in many cases the subjects were drawn from those attending child guidance or psychiatric clinics. Naturally those who are found in these clinics tend to suffer from psychological troubles; and if, on investigation, it turns out that a fair proportion of such cases have a history of maternal deprivation or

separation, this history readily becomes suspect as a possible " etiological factor ".

In order to estimate the weight of such an etiological factor, it is
obviously necessary to know the incidence in the population at large of
comparable infantile experiences. It is therefore much to be regretted
that Dr Bowlby has apparently decided to give up as hopeless any
attempt to get light on this essential quantitative aspect of his problem.
To survey an adequate sample of the general population in order to
discover both the incidence of separation experiences and the frequency
with which these appear to cause damage that is both serious and lasting
would be in Bowlby's view

> " an undertaking of such magnitude as to lie outside the limit of feasibility.
> Whether it would be worth undertaking on a more superficial basis is doubtful...
> On the other hand, starting with the assumption that separation has already been
> shown to be a pathogenic factor, it might fruitfully be used to answer certain socio-
> logical questions: Where in the population does separation occur most frequently
> and in connexion with what problems ? " [1]

This is certainly a counsel of despair as well as a grave breakdown in
logic. The assumption that separation is a pathogenic factor cannot be
substantiated unless and until it is demonstrated that the pathological
symptoms appear more frequently among the separated than among the
non-separated. No matter how intensively we may study the experience
of those among the separated who are known to suffer from such symptoms, we can never assess the pathogenic nature of that experience so
long as we have no idea how often others with similar histories manage
to make out at least as well as the rest of us. To attempt such an assessment in the absence of this vital information is on a par with trying to
calculate the insurance premiums to be charged for fire risks by reference only to those houses which have actually caught fire.

Finally there remains the problem of distinguishing between deprivation and separation. For obvious practical reasons separation is a
much more tractable subject of investigation than is rejection or deprivation: research therefore tends to concentrate upon the former, thus
ignoring the fact that, as Howells has observed, " the greater number of
children who are deprived of mothering are in fact living with the mother
and are not separated from her. " [13] Bowlby is himself well aware of the
importance of this distinction. Nevertheless in one of the most recent
statements of his position he maintains that, although were he now to
revise his monograph he would need to take account of various subsequent criticisms, the practical recommendations would stand. " In
my judgment the separation of a young child from his mother-figure is not
to be undertaken without weighty reasons, and then only provided
there is a suitable and stable substitute available to care for him." [6]

To sum up, therefore, I can only repeat, in the words of the conclusion reached in my book, that up to the present research into effects of maternal deprivation is to be valued chiefly for its incidental exposure of the prevalence of deplorable patterns of institutional upbringing, and of the crass indifference of certain hospitals to childish sensitivities. Without doubt this research has already had excellent practical effects in stimulating many of the authorities responsible for children's homes and hospitals to change their ways for the better. Meanwhile, it is clear that, where the old bad methods survive, the children, as one would expect, suffer according to their temperaments and circumstances in various ways and in various degrees. Now and again their deprivation seems to express itself in a well-marked pattern of indifference to everybody except themselves, of which one of the expressions is repeated stealing. More than this, however, we cannot say. That the damage is life-long or irreversible, or that maternal deprivation is a major factor in criminal behaviour, must be regarded as unproven hypotheses.

REFERENCES

1. Ainsworth, M. D. & Bowlby, J. (1954) Research strategy in the study of mother-child separation. *Courrier*, **4**, No. 3, 2

2. Andry, R. G. (1955) *A comparative psychological study of parent/child relationships as associated with delinquency*, London (Thesis — unpublished manuscript), p. 357

3. Bowlby, J. (1946) *Forty-four juvenile thieves, their characters and home life*, London, Baillière, Tindall & Cox

4. Bowlby, J. (1952) *Maternal care and mental health*, 2nd ed., Geneva (*World Health Organization: Monograph Series*, No. 2)

5. Bowlby, J. (1958) [Letter to the Editor]. *Lancet*, **1**, 1070

6. Bowlby, J. (1958) Note on mother-child separation as a mental health hazard *Brit. J. med. Psychol.*, **31**, 247

7. Bowlby, J., Ainsworth, M., Boston, M. & Rosenbluth, D. (1956) The effects of mother-child separation: a follow-up study. *Brit. J. med. Psychol.*, **29**, 211

8. Douglas, J. W. B. & Blomfield, J. M. (1958) *Children under five*, London, Allen & Unwin

9. Edelston, H. (1952) *The earliest stages of delinquency*, Edinburgh, Livingstone

10. Glueck, S. & Glueck, E. T. (1940) *Juvenile delinquents grown up*, New York, Commonwealth Fund, p. 108

11. Glueck, S. & Glueck, E. T. (1950) *Unraveling juvenile delinquency*, Cambridge, Mass., Harvard University Press, p. 122

12. Howells, J. G. (1958) [Letter to the Editor]. *Lancet*, **1**, 691

13. Howells, J. G. (1959) Children in hospital. *Brit. med. J.*, **1**, 1119

14. *Int. Child Welf. Rev.*, 1959, No. 1, p. 8 (Report on children's institutions in Holland)

15. Lewis, H. (1954) *Deprived children (the Mershal experiment). A social and clinical study*, London, Oxford University Press

16. Mead, M. (1954) Some theoretical considerations on the problem of mother-child separation. *Amer. J. Orthopsychiat.*, **24**, 471

17. Naess, S. (1959) Mother-child separation and delinquency. *Brit. J. Delinq.*, **10**, 22

18. National Association for Mental Health (1949) *Why delinquency? Report of the Conference on the Scientific Study of Juvenile Delinquency*, London, p. 36

19. Rowntree, G. (1955) Early childhood in broken families. *Populat. Stud.*, **8,** 247

20. Stott, D. H. (1956) The effects of separation from the mother in early life. *Lancet*, **1**, 624

21. Tanner, J. M. & Inhelder, B., ed. (1956) *Discussions on child development*, London, Tavistock Publications. Vol. 2, p. 228 [Proceedings of the Second Meeting of the WHO Study Group on the Psychobiological Development of the Child, London, 1954]

22. Taylor, F. Kräupl (1958) [Letter to the Editor]. *Lancet*, **1**, 643

23. Wootton, B. (1959) *Social science and social pathology*, London, Allen & Unwin

THE CONCEPT OF MATERNAL DEPRIVATION:
A REVIEW OF RESEARCH

S. LEBOVICI *

Freud was the first to draw attention to the importance of early emotional experience in the causation of mental disorders in the adults whom he treated by psychoanalysis. Later applications of psychoanalysis to younger and younger children led to reconstruction and interpretation of the early phases of the object relationship that comes into being between an infant and its mother. The maturation of the nervous system, which continues for some considerable time after birth, leads to a succession of experiences in which at first the mother figure takes shape only in connexion with need. When the infant, his hunger satisfied, is capable of recognizing her, he can obviously form a picture of the mother object, distinguish it from himself and differentiate himself as a separate entity ("autonomization"). This is a fundamental period for the child's later mental development, and everything suggestst hat it occurs towards the end of the first year of life. Any later distress or anxiety is capable of jeopardizing the basis of this object relationship: external and internal danger leads to anxiety lest the relationship disintegrate.

The behaviour of the child does not result solely from the maturation of his nervous system: the object relationship also plays a part in development. Any uncertainties and failings it may have and the emotional deprivation that underlies them are bound to have an unfavourable effect on his development.

Research on emotional deprivation has been pursued for some years, on the theoretical foundations thus very briefly outlined, and the conclusion has been reached that only maternal care is capable of preventing the long-term consequences of early emotional frustrations.

Numerous research workers have engaged in the theoretical study of these problems or approached them experimentally, clinically or statistically, but it is to Bowlby that credit is due for having examined them again systematically. A thorough analysis of Bowlby's monograph,[10]

* Secretary-General, Institute of Psychoanalysis, Paris, France; WHO Consultant in Child Psychiatry.

in which his work is embodied, would not be appropriate here. Only an outline of it will be given, with special emphasis on Part I (dealing with the adverse effects of maternal deprivation), and in particular on the review of the basic works on the effects of early emotional deprivation.

The author begins by noting that in physiology harmful factors seem to have a particularly serious effect when they act upon an organ during the earliest stages of its development. There is a striking resemblance between this biological principle and the principle stated by the psychiatrists when they attribute long-term effects to certain emotional experiences occurring during the early stages of psychological development — i.e., from the first six months of life onwards.

Direct observations of emotional deprivation are very numerous. Some deal with the mental health and development of children placed in institutions, hospitals and foster-homes. Others constitute a retrospective study of the early childhood of patients suffering from mental disorders. Others again are follow-up studies of groups of children who have suffered emotional deprivation in their early years. The direct study of the consequences of maternal deprivation has been the subject of a considerable number of papers, particularly by Burlingham & Freud,[17, 18] on children placed in a Hampstead residential nursery during the bombing of London, and by Spitz[56, 57] and Spitz & Wolf.[58] A paper by Bakwin[4] mentions other researches and gives a general review of paediatric literature on the subject.

In 1943 and in subsequent years Goldfarb[24-26] had an opportunity of studying communities of children in institutions. An investigation of the IQs of 30 children aged 34-35 months clearly showed that 15 of the children, who had been brought up in institutions, had IQs lower by 28 points than those of the remaining 15, who had been in foster-homes from the age of four months. These results, which are statistically valid, have been confirmed by the later research of Roudinesco & Appell.[53]

Spitz gives the name of " anaclitic depression " to the state of dazed stupor found in children deprived of maternal care. The child is apathetic, silent and sad; it makes no attempt at contact; in many cases it suffers from insomnia, it loses weight and becomes prone to intercurrent infections; there is a rapid drop in the developmental quotient. This syndrome seems to be characteristic of children who have had a harmonious emotional relationship with their mothers up to the age of six months. Of the 95 children studied by Spitz this type of depression was observed in almost 50%. Recovery is rapid if the child is restored to its mother, but after three months of deprivation recovery is rarely, if ever, complete.

Burlingham & Freud studied older children. They reported that the " separation in slow stages " that they attempted to carry out only produced beneficial effects in children at least three years old but could do nothing to prevent regression in younger children. Maternal deprivation has less serious repercussions as children grow older, although the effects of emotional frustration make themselves felt to a very late stage.

It will be readily understood that retrospective studies in fact preceded the direct study of the consequences of maternal deprivation. As long ago as 1937 Levy [40] described the case of an eight-year-old girl who, after she had been adopted, was brought to him because of her stealing. She had been cared for by a succession of foster-mothers, and her characristic features were the superficiality of her social relationships, her incapacity to form attachments and her lack of emotional responsiveness.

A few years later numerous authors published observations of the same nature. Among them Lauretta Bender,[6] Goldfarb [24] and Bowlby [8] can be mentioned in particular. After the Second World War, Bender [5] returned to the problem, describing the syndrome to which she gave the name " psychopathic behaviour disorder of childhood ". Bowlby,[9] in his book on forty-four juvenile thieves, insists particularly on the tendency to steal in such children. It will be recalled that the forty-four juvenile thieves differed from the children in the control group by their affectionless behaviour. Almost half of them had suffered complete separation for six months or more during the first five years of their life, whereas only two of the controls had suffered similar separations.

Follow-up studies are of particular interest. One of the most important was carried out by Goldfarb,[26] who chose two groups of children of similar heredity. Those in the first group had been brought up in institutions until the age of three and then placed in the care of foster-mothers, whereas those in the second group had been handed over to foster-mothers from the outset. In all cases separation had taken place within the first nine months of life. The lack of intellectual ability and particularly the ability to conceptualize were particularly marked in the group sent to an institution at an early age.

The body of research done on this question is summarized in the first chapters of Bowlby's monograph, after which certain interim conclusions are drawn. The author then analyses the theoretical problems posed by the research already done and the further investigations needed. A careful reading of the monograph shows how circumspectly Bowlby formulates these theoretical problems.

RECENT RESEARCH

Since the publication of Bowlby's monograph research has gone deeper into the problem. The concepts of maternal deprivation, early emotional frustration and the ill effects of institutionalization have gained wide currency. The conditions under which children live in hospitals and institutions have been the subject of numerous studies, which have certainly played a part in the improvement of material and psychological conditions. In general, as has just been said, these investigations have confirmed the results of the original research. Certain authors have, however, disagreed on a number of points, generally in connexion with one particular aspect of the problem. No claim is made to present in this chapter a complete review of all the papers published since Bowlby's monograph appeared. In analysing the trends apparent in some of them which have come to our attention, only passing reference will be made to the problems that still await solution.

It must be emphasized that the importance of the idea of maternal deprivation is apparent from all these studies, whatever their value— even those which do not fully confirm the general hypotheses formulated by Bowlby. The growing interest of many specialists who are concerned to a greater or lesser extent with emotionally deprived children has, in fact, proved useful. Paediatricians, for example, have ceased to be preoccupied solely with the control of physical disease in hospitals. The psychological conditions of hospital life and their emotional consequences have been dealt with in a number of interesting papers (e.g., those by Robertson, Rosenbluth & Bowlby,[52] Edelston,[20] Bakwin,[4] Davidson,[19] Faust,[22] Jackson,[32] MacKeith,[43] Moncrieff & Walton,[45] Pickerill & Pickerill,[47] and Powers.[48] A film on this subject, entitled " A Two-Year-Old Goes to Hospital ", has been made by Robertson [51] and his colleagues; it is a study of the behaviour of a little girl, aged two years five months, during an eight days' stay in hospital. The purpose of this film, a purely scientific document, is to present objective data on the behaviour of the child in the hospital ward by noting her attitudes, her relationships with the nurses and her reactions towards her parents during their visits. Information on the attitudes of the child in her family during the subsequent months is given by the author in the literature accompanying the film. Finally, it should be mentioned that in September 1954 the Regional Office for Europe of the World Health Organization convened in Stockholm a meeting of a study group in which paediatricians and psychiatrists discussed together the problems of children in hospital.[39]

If the various researches on the consequences of maternal deprivation had merely succeeded in drawing the attention of many categories of professional worker and even of families to the problem, that in itself would be a matter for congratulation. It is right that some thought should be given to the consequences of placing infants in day nurseries; the policy of placing children in children's homes and boarding institutions for social reasons deserves discussion. Stays by children in an open-air centre *(aérium)* or a preventorium are often useless and may even be harmful. It has become more and more apparent that very often the placing of children in these various types of institution is advised on the grounds of social and economic difficulties in their families. It may be wondered whether the social welfare service should not be completely reoriented: the policy of creating institutions that sooner or later have ill effects on those sent to them should be replaced by long-term planning to build many more houses and to provide assistance for mothers who have to go out to work. This is the sort of conclusion that seems finally to have been reached by all those who have had occasion to reflect on these problems, even though certain authorities, as will be seen, consider that sometimes too much importance is attached to the idea of the ill effects of institutionalization.

In order to sum up recent research and criticism on the problems posed by maternal deprivation, reference will first be made to a number of definitions on which Bowlby bases his work; this will be followed by brief accounts of some investigations and discussions on the subject.

Ainsworth & Bowlby [1] have defined research strategy in the study of the consequences of mother-child separation. They found their argument on a body of theoretical assumptions, the psychoanalytic basis of which is integrated into more general neurobiological theory. These authors recall the importance of the mother-child object relationship as defined by M. Klein [33-35] in the sphere of psychoanalysis. They emphasize, from the etiological point of view, the ethological studies of Lorenz [41, 42] and Tinbergen, [60] which demonstrate the relationship between instinct and object relations. They point out that Hunt [31] and Scott et al. [54, 55] have shown that in the training of the higher animals critical phases of development influence the whole of the rest of their lives. They emphasize that numerous authors have noted the irreversibility of responses learnt under stress.

In their study the authors recall Bowlby's initial hypothesis:

"...actual physical separation from the mother in early childhood, to the extent that it involves privation or deprivation of a relationship of dependence with a mother-figure, will have an adverse effect on personality development, particularly with resrect to the capacity for forming and maintaining satisfactory object relations. "

Such a relationship may be inadequate under three conditions:

(1) where the child never has any relationship with a mother-person;

(2) where the relationship with the mother-person is discontinuous;

(3) where the relationship with the mother-person is insecure.

The first two conditions imply real separation, either through absence (privation) or through loss (deprivation). A child only gradually becomes dependent on a single person. It is at the moment when he has reached dependence that the effects of separation seem the most dangerous. At a later stage, on the other hand, the child's " autonomization " requires that he should be capable of bearing at least temporary separation. The authors therefore suggest the following classification for defining the conditions of separation of the child from its mother:

" (1)   Separation from the mother *before* a stable and secure dependency relationship has been established, with

(*a*)   lack of subsequent opportunity to form a stable relationship with any one mother-figure, as in institutionalization — the case of *complete privation;* or

(*b*)   a temporary lack of opportunity to form a stable relationship with any one mother-figure but with later opportunity to establish one either with the natural mother or with a mother-substitute — the case of *temporary privation* of greater or lesser duration; or

(*c*)   immediate substitution for the mother of a substitute mother with whom the child can establish a stable and secure relationship, as in early adoption; this probably results *in no appreciable privation.*

(2)   Separation from the mother (or substitute mother) *after* a stable and secure dependency relationship has been established and before the child is old enough to be independent of the mother, with

(*a*)   severance of the relationship and no subsequent opportunity to form a stable and secure relationship with the original or a substitute figure — the most severe case of *deprivation;* or

(*b*)   severance of the relationship but with opportunity to form a stable and secure relationship with a substitute mother; despite the provision of the substitute figure this may involve *temporary deprivation* through the very breach of relationship; or

(*c*)   a temporary interruption of the relationship followed by reunion with the mother. This case is also one of *temporary deprivation...*"

The authors point out that this classification is only an outline and that actual case analysis should take into account numerous factors, such as the intimacy of the relationship with the mother before the separation, the length of the separation, the nature of the father-child relationship, etc.

The authors then turn to the study of the possible methods of approach and discuss four that had already been envisaged in Bowlby's monograph.

Systematic case study

This method requires the use of statistical tests to confirm the hypothesis of a connexion between the syndrome observed and the separation of the child from its mother. It was in fact the first method used, showing that the early separation of a child from its mother led to a lack of capacity to establish any but shallow relationships and that it could be responsible for antisocial or asocial behaviour. In this connexion Bowlby's work on the forty-four juvenile thieves [9] and Bender's study of psychopathic behaviour disorders [5] are quoted.

The retrospective follow-up method

This approach may provide an answer to uncertainties not resolved by systematic case study, such as, for example, when a case is encountered in which early separation has not produced the predicted effects. In retrospective studies the group is homogeneous in respect of the antecedent factor of separation, whereas in systematic case study it is homogeneous in respect of the observed effects. The work by Goldfarb [26] mentioned earlier was based on research of this type. Comparison with control groups is essential, and attention should be drawn to several inherent difficulties: first, the etiological factors under study together represent an extreme case; secondly, the selection of control groups is extremely difficult. (Spitz [56] provided a very ingenious model for comparing two institutional groups; in only one of the groups were the infants separated from their mothers.) A further difficulty is due to the uncertainty that must inevitably attend any effort to assess the condition of the patients studied: psychometric and testing methods are inadequate. Clinical interviews require the creation of a real therapeutic atmosphere.

The " current study " method

This method is based on the study of children actually undergoing a separation experience and followed up right from the outset. In this way very varied observations can be grouped together and children can be kept under observation for as long as is wished. In this case also, however, it is essential to go beyond the stage of general investigation. The authors recall the work of Spitz,[56, 58] showing that the damage caused by a separation of five months in the second six months of life is probably irreparable. Aubry-Roudinesco [3] considers that the following proposition can be formulated: the decline in developmental quotient is proportionate to the logarithm of the length of separation. In this type of research Ainsworth & Bowlby suggest that three periods should be studied:

(1) *Before separation*, in which the nature of the mother-child relationship and the degree of dependence on the mother-figure would be brought out.

(2) *During separation*, in which it would be important to find out the immediate effects and the degree of the child's adjustment to what might be called the " separation environment ".

(3) *After separation*, in which observations would cover not only the effects of separation itself but also those due to the return to the original

environment or the entry into a new environment which provides a mother-substitute.

The study by Burlingham & Freud [17], [18] and the research by two teams working jointly under the auspices of the International Children's Centre (under the direction of Bowlby in England and Aubry-Roudinesco in France) have been based on this research method.

At this point the authors report the first results of their research on children whose relationships with their mother before separation had been good. They describe three phases of separation: protest, despair and negativism (or repression). It seems to them that the form of the response to reunion depends on the form of the response to separation.

The psychoanalytic research study

This seems of interest to the authors not so much because of the possibilities offered of reconstructing the past as because the psycho-analytic session provides an experimental situation in which the behaviour of a child can be studied either during the separation itself or after it.

The paper by Ainsworth & Bowlby has been analysed here because it seems to provide a fairly complete frame of reference for the classification of the research now to be mentioned. The questions dealt with in particular will be research on the adverse effects of institutionalization, clinical work on the establishment of object relationships, experimental research on animals and man, and follow-up studies that seem to have aroused a great deal of discussion.

ADVERSE EFFECTS OF INSTITUTIONALIZATION

In general, the work published on this subject has largely confirmed that of Spitz. Thus, in her book *La Carence de Soins Maternels*, Aubry-Roudinesco [3] describes the results of a multidisciplinary study of a group of children in the care of the Administration de l'Assistance Publique in Paris, at the Fondation Parent de Rosan. The first part of the book, which deals with methods, describes the research techniques used, including medical, paediatric and psychological observation, the last of these based on the Gesell test. The results of separation are described in the second part of the book, which states that physical condition, morbidity and psychomotor development are all affected by separation. The author studies the consequences of separation under the name of " distress reaction ", of which she describes numerous clinical aspects.

For his part, Spitz in numerous studies has been able to go more deeply into the clinical basis of the ill effects of life in institutions. He has been particularly concerned with the description of what he calls " psychotoxic syndromes "—specific somatic syndromes corresponding to early emotional frustrations experienced at different ages.[57] In his introductory report to the 4th International Conference on Child Psychiatry at Lisbon in 1958, Spitz quoted some statistical data which confirmed the seriousness of the adverse effects of institutionalization he had made in his first observations. Thus, in his report (which has not yet been published) he revealed that out of 91 children of whom it had been possible to keep track, 37.5% had died before the age of two years. Spitz was able to follow up 21 of the 91 children until the age of four. At that age, 20 of them could not dress themselves without assistance, 15 had only very inadequately acquired habits of cleanliness and six had no sphincter control. From the language point of view, six could not speak a single word, five only had a vocabulary of two words and only one could make up sentences. These facts offer sufficient confirmation of the seriousness of the effects of life in institutions.

Despite the interest of these follow-up investigations into the ill effects of institutionalization, some authors do not seem absolutely convinced. Heuyer,[28] while recognizing the importance of Spitz's work, thought that in describing states of deterioration in institutionalized infants, not enough attention had been paid to the possibility of an undiagnosed encephalopathy. The same author, in his introductory report on the somatic aspects of child psychiatry at the 4th International Conference on Child Psychiatry, stated that at a previous conference maternal deprivation had served as an explanation for all the behaviour disorders of the child, without the trouble being taken even to make a diagnosis, to study the child's past history, to make full use of biological and physiological investigations, and to draw up a scheme of individual treatment. The result has been a hotch-potch of verbal explanations of no great practical value. Heuyer thought that the concept of adverse effects arising from institutionalization was undoubtedly of interest. However, after daily repeated examination of children retarded in their physical and emotional development, he felt he could state definitely that he had never seen a pure case of the adverse effects of institutional life.

Other authors have put forward much less thorough-going criticisms than those of Heuyer. Thus Launay and his colleagues,[36] while recognizing the frequency of reactive disorders following separation from the mother upon entering hospital, and accepting the description of halts in development and seeming backwardness followed by total recovery, consider nevertheless that no final disintegration of the personality can be observed in these children. In their opinion, some of the children were probably suffering from infantile encephalopathy. Launay considers that the dramatic picture of anaclitic depression, the reality of which cannot be doubted, " seems to paediatricians used to hospital paediatric services and children's homes to occur very rarely ".

The less stark picture painted by these authors is, in their view, more frequent and consists essentially of initial upset after separation. The child reacts noisily but the reaction only lasts a few hours or a few days. Return to the family produces a cessation of symptoms. Readjustment takes longer only in the more anxious types of children. If separation occurs again, the child's reaction is less noisy and takes the form of apathy with regression.

Launay and his colleagues consider that regressions due to institutional life are encountered mainly in undernourished infants, with a weight very much below normal for their age owing either to congenital debility or to antecedent illness, accompanied in general by inadequate care. Developmental quotients not exceeding 50 are habitually found in such cases. Generally the children's mental state improves in step with their physical condition.

In the case of other children, the effect of hospitalization varies. Some may regress a little, others appear hardly different on discharge from what they were when admitted, and some may even show considerable progress because of the poor conditions of their previous life. The diversity of the consequences of hospitalization is obviously due to several factors: the conditions in the hospital and particularly the attitude of the nursing staff to the children, the conditions of family life before admission, the individual characteristics of each child and even its physical appearance (an attractive and intelligent child, for example, will be made much of by the nurses and will suffer less than the others from its stay in hospital).

Bertoye [7] draws conclusions very similar to those of Launay. For example, he writes: " There remains a large number of children who show various degrees of abnormality in their psychomotor behaviour; this abnormality must be considered as having existed before their admission to the nursery."

In conclusion, the first descriptions by Spitz of the evil effects of institutionalization, their break-down into specific clinical and etiological forms, and their later confirmation by other authors form a striking picture and have made an immense contribution to social paediatrics. The most specific criticisms only affect details and consist in general of concepts or observations underlining the inconstancy or the varying seriousness of the trauma. In some cases, the authors show that a stay in hospital may have an educative or even a therapeutic effect. Here a distinction must obviously be drawn between the case of the older child, whose separation from his parents is useful or even essential (as has long been appreciated in psychiatry—e.g., in cases of psychogenic anorexia), and that of the infant—the only case studied by Spitz—in which separation at the end of the first year of life without the provision of a mother-substitute can have catastrophic consequences.

The seriousness of this latter type of case can be better understood on the basis of the hypotheses set forth below concerning the establishment of object relationships.

CLINICAL AND THEORETICAL RESEARCH
ON THE ESTABLISHMENT OF OBJECT RELATIONSHIPS

It will be recalled that Bowlby submitted as his basic hypothesis the idea that early separation from the mother constituted a serious and lasting impediment to the establishment of solid and secure object relationships. Spitz's findings, based on direct observation of groups of children, statistically analysed and supported by filmed evidence, show that the crucial period for the establishment of true object relationships occurs in the second half of the first six months of a child's life. During the first few months the child lives with its mother in a pre-object relationship which is based only on its needs and the anonymous satisfaction it receives. The smile at the sight of the mother's face is the first trace of a true relationship between mother and child, and is observed from the third month onwards. Towards the ninth month the child is capable of recognizing its mother without needing her. Spitz observed during this period real manifestations of anxiety when the mother disappeared.

Lebovici & Diatkine [38] studied afresh, on a theoretical basis, the first object relationships of the child. In their work on the study of child phantasies it was shown that phantasy images of disintegration are only the later elaboration of the first experiences in which the infant, incapable of recognizing himself as a body, can only conceive of his mother in a partial fragmentary way, the parts not being differentiated from but confused with himself. In a confused relationship, which develops gradually in time but which is merely a functional relationship only manifesting itself in case of need, the child becomes aware of his mother as a nourishment object with which he seeks total fusion. As his maturation progresses he becomes aware of his own body, at the moment when he is capable of recognizing the body of the other person —i.e., that of his mother. It is thus that the first object relationships are established on the basis of pre-object relationships that are solely functional. When the object relationship has taken shape, a real rudimentary psychological life linking the child to his mother can be considered to have begun.

Lebovici & Diatkine [38] in a study of obsessions in children, investigated the significance of functional games of the end of the infant's first year. Thus, when a child drops an object in order to experience the jubilant satisfaction of having it picked up by his mother, he is assuring himself of his power over her. He shows us at the same time that he is capable of having a certain mental picture of the object here symbolized by the toy: he assures himself that when the object has gone he can make it come back. Thus this game is the basis of what psychoanalysts call object hallucination.

This very rapid and cursory sketch of the theories of the genesis of object relationships shows clearly that separation from the mother is particularly dangerous at the time when a true object relationship has been established—i.e., at the end of the first year of life. In the first six months of life the mother is only a functional object, whose presence is essential, or at least so it appears, only in case of need. A whole range of maternal contributions seems, however, to be necessary to establish the later bases for a valid object relationship. (This will be discussed again later.) But it is at the moment when the child recognizes his mother as such that she is indispensable to him, and that maternal deprivation through loss is likely to have the most fateful consequences.

This theory of the early aspects of the object relationship is founded not only on direct observation of the child but also on data provided by neurobiological studies of children. It has given rise to much research by psychoanalysts (in America, by the school of genetic psychoanalysis —H. Hartmann, E. Kris and R. Loewenstein, as well as René Spitz; [57] in Great Britain, by Anna Freud in her studies in psychoanalytic psychology; and in France, by Ajuriaguerra et al.[2] and Lebovici[37]. The basic idea can be summarized as follows: the establishment of an object relationship is a consequence of the child's dependence—i.e., its state of incomplete maturity at birth. It must therefore be postulated that the object is encountered and experienced before even being perceived. It is on the basis of a stage of initial lack of differentiation that this development is possible. This theory of primary dependency in many ways confirms the Freudian hypothesis of early narcissism.

In a series of recent works Bowlby has criticized this attempt to integrate psychoanalytic studies with the body of neurobiological knowledge. He bases his work, on the contrary, on the hypothesis of a primary object relation put forward by the psychoanalysts of the so-called Hungarian school (A. & M. Balint). They prefer the concept of attachment —the existence of which they claim to be confirmed by much ethological research—to that of dependence. The attachment of the infant to its mother brings about a real " monotropy " which, according to Bowlby, goes far beyond the sphere of oral needs. Primary object attachment, he holds, is expressed in a certain number of instinctual responses which appear at successive periods in time, as can be explained by the theory of innate releasing mechanisms. Five components are essentially involved: sucking, clinging, following, crying, and smiling. All these enable the child to survive, since they elicit the maternal care needed and permit intimate contact between infant and mother.

In this work on the nature of the ties between the child and its mother, Bowlby [11] therefore rejects the dependency theory and the theory of secondary tie to support not only the theory of the Kleinian psychoanalytic school (primary object sucking or primary attachment to the mother's breast) but also and especially the theory of primary object attachment, which seems to him to take into account the ethological evidence, such as the research on genetic psychology carried out by Piaget.

More recently still, Bowlby [14] has studied the consequences of separation between mother and child at a later age. He thinks that these are more important than is generally believed—separation puts in jeopardy the instinctual bonds and triggers off the "work of mourning" very similar to that observed in adults. Finally the anxiety of the child seems to Bowlby [15] to be the consequence of the breaking of these same bonds.

There can be nothing but agreement on the need to extend the description of mother-child relationships at the anaclitic, pre-object stages far beyond the oral and alimentary sphere, despite its predominant value in psychoanalytic reconstruction. Rather than speculate about the part played by innate releasing mechanisms, whose nature we only know in reference to the ethological study of the decoy, it is preferable to take one's stand on an indisputable fact: the incomplete maturity of the infant places it in a state of need and dependence. Differentiation is achieved within the relationship that specifies the object at the same time as the self. It goes without saying that instinctual attachment behaviour, whose existence can legitimately be acknowledged, strengthens this tie.

EXPERIMENTAL RESEARCH ON MATERNAL DEPRIVATION
IN MAN AND ANIMALS

Reference is made here to a number of experimental studies which tend to show that insufficiency of stimuli approximating (other things being equal) to deprivation of maternal care seems to have a significant effect in man and animals.

Donald Hebb has studied dogs reared in complete isolation from their mother. He claims that they become stupid and abnormal and, above all, that they have no aptitude for learning, drawing no profit from painful experiences to which they are subjected.

Benjamin, Bernstein and Conger describe the following experiment, made on two equal groups of rats of identical origins. The experiments began on the 20th day after weaning. The first group of rats were stroked for 10 minutes a day, while the rats in the second group were reared in complete isolation. The rats in the second group developed less well than those which had been stroked. On the 40th day of the experiment it was found that they were less capable of learning. Their weight was lower, although they ate and excreted more. When they were sacrificed, it was found that they succumbed to a dose of thiouracil which was two or three times lower than that required to kill the stroked rats. The adrenal glands of the isolated rats were of greater weight, which the experimenters attributed to greater distress. The comparisons drawn between the two groups of rats are statistically valid.

Hebb arranged an experiment in which a group of volunteers were totally deprived of tactile, visual and auditory stimuli for several days. On coming out of their isolation the volunteers showed a very marked diminution in capacity for learning. They stated that during the experiment they had had hallucinations accompanied by a genuine confusional state. Asima was able to repeat this experiment with insane patients. In some cases the experiment proved beneficial, while in others it triggered off an acute psychotic episode after four or five days.

These experiments, which are described by Spitz, certainly deserve detailed study. A good proportion of them should undoubtedly be repeated in greater detail. It is, however, useful to quote them since they apparently show clearly the importance of stimulation in the development of personality. They explain why the concept of maternal deprivation is being replaced more and more by the idea of frustration and emotional deprivation, which is, of course, much less precise, although its consequences are accepted by very many psychiatrists.

FOLLOW-UP STUDIES OF MATERNAL DEPRIVATION

Some of the accounts of experiments mentioned above may appear open to criticism on the grounds of imprecision, but the workers who have devoted all their activities to studying the consequences of maternal deprivation have been very exacting in regard to their own work. This applies particularly to Bowlby. It will be recalled that in the work on research strategy analysed at length earlier in this chapter, Bowlby proposed that follow-up studies should be as thorough as possible. Naturally, as this work has developed certain hypotheses have had to be reformulated. The work of the team in question is reflected in correspondence published in the *Lancet* in 1958. Correspondents had criticized an article published in the *British Journal of Medical Psychology* [16] in which a comparison was made between the personality of children placed in a sanatorium before the age of four and that of classmates who had not been separated from their families. The comparison was based on teachers' reports and on psychological testing. It was found that certain children in the group placed in the sanatorium before the age of four were capable of contracting ties of friendship and did not appear to be suffering from the serious disorders in object relationship that underlie delinquency. Although there were significant differences, Bowlby concluded that it could not be asserted that children lodged in an institution in their early childhood in general presented a psychotic or affectionless character.

This article raised a controversy in which, on the one hand, the study itself was attacked, while, on the other, in a more general way the importance of the whole concept of maternal deprivation came under fire. For example, in his letter to the *Lancet*, Taylor [59] indicates that the study of the groups of children had been inadequate. For instance, no account had been taken of the fact that there were twice as many boys as girls in the sample of 57 children involved. Almost half the teachers' reports had been discarded as not seeming sufficiently reliable. Taylor wondered whether the discarding procedure was not due to a desire to prove the validity of the initial hypotheses. In the same way, he pointed out that only 31 psychologists' reports had been retained, but that it had not been stated whether these referred to the children on whom the teachers' reports had also been retained.

In the same correspondence, Howells [29] criticized the study in question in the light of Bowlby's own concepts. He thought that a distinction should have been drawn in the sanatorium group of children between the effects of separation from the mother and the effects of deprivation in the sanatorium. Howells recalled a study that he had published in 1955,[30] in which he compared a group of emotionally disturbed children and a control group of healthy children, by studying their separation experiences before the age of five years. No significant difference was found. He thereupon concluded that it is not separation that is necessarily injurious but rather privation. Privation need not arise after separation, and may, in any case, exist even though the mother is present. Howells concluded by pointing out that children may suffer privation of maternal care in the family, whereas improved organization of children's hospitals, nurseries, etc., would doubtless make it possible to eliminate many of the effects of such privation.

Edelston,[21] when he intervened in this correspondence, supported Howells' point of view. He recalled a quip of Margaret Mead's [44] to the effect that the campaign against maternal deprivation has become a subtle form of antifeminism in which men, under the guise of exalting the importance of maternity, are tying women more tightly to their children.

Bowlby intervened in this correspondence on several occasions. It will be recalled that in his opinion the principal value of the study of the two groups of children concerned had been to display the great heterogeneity of personality organization in the group of children who had undergone a prolonged separation starting before the fourth birthday. Very modestly, he stated that if he had to prepare a revised edition of *Maternal Care and Mental Health* he would include in Part I, which deals with research on the adverse effects of maternal deprivation, many new studies, of which most, but not all, confirmed the initial hypotheses.

In his final letter [13] in reply to his critics, Bowlby acknowledged the importance of the difference between separation and deprivation, but maintained that they were both adverse factors, neither of which should be neglected, and that separation could not but affect the emotional attachment between child and mother. Stays with relatives and friends, when the child is separated from his own family, might not have bad effects, but very often a child experienced acute distress which increased cumulatively with successive moves. He therefore remained convinced that a child should be separated from his mother only in exceptional circumstances.

In his first letter [12] he had said that some people appeared to think that he no longer regarded the separation of young children from their mothers as serious. This was not so, he stated in the conclusion to this letter; he simply wished to discourage anyone from supposing that he had changed his position in any material way.

CONCLUSIONS

Thus, research workers interested in the consequences of maternal deprivation have been able to give more precision to their theories, partly because they have gone deeper with their studies and experiments and partly because they have had to take into account the arguments of those whose observations sometimes contradicted their original hypotheses. It remains true, however, that maternal deprivation in young children is a serious matter with serious consequences and requires a co-ordinated social policy to deal with it.

It would indeed be highly dangerous to attribute the overwhelming majority of emotional and mental disorders in adolescents and adults to such deprivation: that would be a great step backwards, to a time when it was thought that neuroses and psychoses must be traumatic in origin—a hypothesis that later research did not confirm. Psychopathological structures which have been built up slowly and constantly reshaped obviously cannot be due to a single event, however serious its significance, even if it occurred at a decisive time in the establishment of object relationships. It is nevertheless true that the concept of maternal deprivation has gradually been extended in psychopathology: studies of early frustrations [49], [50] show to what extent.

Knowledge of the consequences of early frustration presupposes the taking into consideration of the needs of the infant for varied stimuli, of which our knowledge is very limited. These needs probably belong to the domain of extraverbal communication. Their importance is explained by the physiological lack of maturity of the newborn baby, which puts it in a state of anaclitic dependence upon its mother. It is not only a question of the need for food. The infant must come into close contact with its mother and receive from her sensory stimulation —visual, vestibular, auditory and cutaneous—that must provide it with certain sensations of contact and warmth, and certain rhythmic sensations. Due regard must be paid to the need for sucking and movement.

The study of frustration pathology now takes into account not only the decisive separation experiences that occur at the time when object relationships are being established, but also privation at an earlier period, known as the pre-object or anaclitic period. The consequences of early frustration on future mental health can be stated only with great caution. The first consequence that was suggested, particularly by Bowlby in his study of forty-four thieves, was the development of a delinquent character. While Kate Friedlander,[23] in her description of the apathetic character, confirms the existence of difficulties in early experiences with the mother, other authors dispute the importance of emotional deprivation. Thus Heuyer in his report to the Lisbon Conference stated that the examination of numerous child and juvenile delinquents enabled him to assert with confidence that maternal deprivation had in most cases played only a subordinate role in the causation of delinquency. This, he added, is the danger in isolating an undoubted fact, for the most part incidental, and treating it as the essential cause.

Early frustrations seem indubitably to play a role in certain pathological character structures. This occurs essentially when there is excessive dependence on other persons by those who, in their never-ending quest for affection, constantly need to have proofs of love given to them. A deep-seated masochism seems to be at work in what have been called " ego distortions ". Nacht [46] considers that such persons have undergone serious early frustrations at the hands of sadistic mothers: in any case their lives are governed completely by frustration, which is expressed in their active and constant demand for affection.

Finally the role of early frustration in the psychoses has been under discussion. It is questionable whether depressive states in the adult can be causally linked with anaclitic depression. The effect of early frustration has been studied particularly in relation to the etiology of schizophrenia. To begin with, the therapeutic value of systematic or empirical mothering is significant in the context of the most varied forms of treatment. Many authors, such as Green,[27] think that the mothers of schizophrenics have a psychotic character structure and are seriously frustrating and rejecting. The consequences of early frustration have also been alleged to play a part in chronic alcoholism, psychosomatic disorders, etc.

Certainly the increasingly important position being accorded to studies of disorders of the object relationship in psychopathological research tends to underline the significance of early frustration. However, the handling of object relationships during psychotherapy does not offer confirmation of the historical value of reconstructions of traumatic events related to separation and privation during the first months of life. These are, at the very least, hypotheses that would require confirmation by means of the whole series of investigations on the consequences of maternal deprivation that have been mentioned here. It must also be said in this connexion that there is great danger involved in assessing the effect of traumatic events in an attempt to explain a psychopathological state whose etiology cannot be anything but complex.

Even if it is impossible as yet to make an exact assessment of the seriousness of maternal deprivation, mental health requirements indicate that everything must be done to avoid it. This is a problem that must be dealt with from the social aspect. Only an improvement in housing and in women's working conditions can lessen and mitigate its consequences. And only under such conditions can the separation of children from their mothers be reduced to a minimum. Sending a child to hospital, for which every possible preparation should be made beforehand, will also be less injurious if hospital buildings are improved and hospital staff suitably trained, if the child is kept occupied, and if its contact with its parents is maintained. In fact, Launay et al.[36] and Lelong & Lebovici[39] have shown that in certain cases a child's stay in hospital or in welcoming institutions can have an educative effect.

In this connexion it should be recalled that, contrary to what hasty popularization has asserted, the principles of psychoanalytic teaching emphasize the importance and usefulness of frustration in the formation of the ego. Only frustrations in the proper doses, so to speak, can enable aggressiveness to turn outwards against external objects instead of turning in against, and thus weakening, the developing ego. Hypothetically speaking, if the child has been sufficiently indulged he needs frustrations. It should be recalled to what extent the anxiety in the ninth month of life, described by Spitz, and the functional games through which it is expressed, are constructive in nature: at this point the child is capable of imagining away its mother's absence and enjoying her presence as an internal image. It is quite clear, however, that to enable the child to make his mother " live " by himself and to look upon her as present when she is absent she must still be largely available.

Several years ago Huxley wrote " Give me good mothers and I shall make a better world ". The converse is true: " Make me a better world and I shall give you good mothers ". The prevention of the effects of maternal deprivation will only be possible when these two requirements can be met.

REFERENCES

1. Ainsworth, M. D. & Bowlby, J. (1954) Research strategy in the study of mother-child separation. *Courrier*, **4**, No. 3, 2

2. Ajuriaguerra, J., Diatkine, R. & Garcia Badaracco (1955) *Psychanalyse et neurobiologie*. In: *Psychanalyse d'aujourd'hui*, Paris, Presses universitaires de France

3. Aubry, J. (1955) *La carence de soins maternels*, Paris, Centre international de l'Enfance

4. Bakwin, H. (1949) Emotional deprivation in infants. *J. Pediat.*, **35**, 512

5. Bender, L. (1947) *Psychopathic behavior disorders in children*. In: Lindner, R. M. & Seliger, R. V., ed., *Handbook of correctional psychology*, New York, Philosophical Library, p. 360

6. Bender, L. & Yarnell, H. (1941) An observation nursery. *Amer. J. Psychiat.*, **97**, 1158

7. Bertoye, P. (1957) Le comportement psychique des nourrissons placés en pouponnière. *Ann. Pédiat.*, **38**, 353

8. Bowlby, J. (1940) The influence of early environment in the development of neurosis and neurotic character. *Int. J. Psycho-Anal.*, **21**, 154

9. Bowlby, J. (1946) *Forty-four juvenile thieves, their characters and home life*, London, Baillière, Tindall & Cox

10. Bowlby, J. (1952) *Maternal care and mental health*, 2nd ed., Geneva (*World Health Organization: Monograph Series*, No. 2)

11. Bowlby, J. (1958) The nature of the child's tie to his mother. *Int. J. Psycho-Anal.*, **39**, 350

12. Bowlby, J. (1958) [Letter to the Editor]. *Lancet*, **1**, 480

13. Bowlby, J. (1958) [Letter to the Editor]. *Lancet*, **1**, 1070

14. Bowlby, J. (1960) Separation anxiety. *Int. J. Psycho-Anal.*, **41**, 89

15. Bowlby, J. (1960) Separation anxiety: a critical review of the literature. *J. Child Psychol. Psychiat.*, **1**, 251

16. Bowlby, J., Ainsworth, M., Boston, M. & Rosenbluth, D. (1956) The effects of mother-child separation: a follow-up study. *Brit. J. med. Psychol.*, **29**, 211

17. Burlingham, D. & Freud, A. (1942) *Young children in wartime*, London, Allen & Unwin

18. Burlingham, D. & Freud, A. (1944) *Infants without families*, London, Allen & Unwin

19. Davidson, E. R. (1949) Play for the hospitalised children. *Amer. J. Nurs.*, **49**, 138

20. Edelston, H. (1943) Separation anxiety in young children: study of hospital cases. *Genet. Psychol. Monogr.*, **28**, 3

21. Edelston, H. (1958) [Letter to the Editor]. *Lancet*, **1**, 797

22. Faust, O. (1952) *Reducing emotional trauma in hospitalized children: a study in psychosomatic pediatrics.* In: Albany Medical College, Departments of Pediatrics and Anesthesiology, *Reducing emotional trauma in hospitalized children*, Albany, p. 1536

23. Friedlander, K. (1945) *The formation of the antisocial character.* In: *Psychoanalytic study of the child*, New York, International Universities Press, Vol. 1, p. 189

24. Goldfarb, W. (1943) Infant rearing and problem behavior. *Amer. J. Orthopsychiat.*, **13**, 249

25. Goldfarb, W. (1945) Effects of psychological deprivation in infancy and subsequent stimulation. *Amer. J. Psychiat.*, **102**, 18

26. Goldfarb, W. (1949) Rorschach test differences between family-reared, institution-reared and schizophrenic children. *Amer J. Orthopsychiat.*, **19**, 624

27. Green, A. (1957) *Les familles de schizophrènes* (Thesis, Paris)

28. Heuyer, G. (1952) L'hospitalisme. *Bull. Psychol.*, **6**, 87

29. Howells, J. G. (1958) [Letter to the Editor]. *Lancet*, **1**, 691

30. Howells, J. G. & Layng, J. (1955) Separation experiences and mental health. *Lancet*, **2**, 285

31. Hunt, J. M. V. (1941) The effects of infant feeding-frustration upon adult hoarding in the albino rat. *J. abnorm. soc. Psychol.*, **36**, 338

32. Jackson, K. (1952) *Psychological preparation as method of reducing emotional trauma of anesthesia in children.* In: Albany Medical College, Departments of Pediatrics and Anesthesiology, *Reducing emotional trauma in hospitalized children*, Albany

33. Klein, M. (1932) *The psycho-analysis of children*, London, Hogarth Press

34. Klein, M. (1948) *Contributions to psycho-analysis, 1921-1945*, London, Hogarth Press

35. Klein, M., Heiman, P., Isaacs, S. & Riviere, J. (1952) *Developments in psychoanalysis*, London, Hogarth Press

36. Launay, C., Verliac, F., Trelat, E., Lyard, D. (1956) Carence de soins maternels dans la petite enfance. *Sem. Hôp. Paris*, **30**, 537

37. Lebovici, S. (1960) *La relation objectale chez l'enfant.* In: *Psychiatrie de l'enfant*, Paris, Presses universitaires de France, Vol. 3

38. Lebovici, S. & Diatkine, R. (1957) Les obsessions chez l'enfant. *Rev. franç. Psychanal.*, **21**, 647

39. Lelong, M. & Lebovici, S. (1955) Problèmes psychologiques et psychopathologiques posés par l'enfant à l'hôpital. *Arch. franç. Pédiat.*, **12**, 1

40. Levy, D. (1937) Primary affect hunger. *Amer. J. Psychiat.*, **94**, 643

41. Lorenz, K. Z. (1937) The companion in the bird's world. *Auk*, **54**, 245

42. Lorenz, K. Z. (1950) The comparative method in studying innate behaviour patterns. In: Danielli, J. F. & Brown, R., ed., *Physiological mechanisms in animal behaviour*, London Cambridge University Press *(Symp. Soc. exp. Biol.*, No. 4), p. 221

43. MacKeith, R. (1953) Children in hospital: preparation for operation. *Lancet*, **2**, 843

44. Mead, M. (1954) Some theoretical considerations on the problem of mother-child separation. *Amer. J. Orthopsychiat.*, **24**, 471

45. Moncrieff, A. A. & Walton, A. M. (1952) Visiting children in hospital. *Brit. med. J.*, **1**, 443

46. Nacht, S. (1958) Causes et mécanismes des déformations névrotiques du Moi. *Rev. franç. Psychanal.*, **22**, 197

47. Pickerill, C. M. & Pickerill, H. P. (1946) Keeping mother and baby together. *Brit. med. J.*, **2**, 337

48. Powers, G. F. (1948) Humanizing hospital experiences. *Amer. J. Dis. Child.*, **76**, 365

49. Racamier, P. C. (1953) Etude clinique des frustrations précoces. *Rev. franç. Psychanal.*, **17**, 328

50. Racamier, P.C. (1954) La pathologie frustrationnelle. *Rev. franç. Psychanal.*, **18**, 576

51. Robertson, J. (1952) *A two-year-old goes to hospital* (Film: 16 mm; 45 min.; sound. Distributors: Tavistock Child Development Research Unit, London; New York University Film Library)

52. Robertson, J., Rosenbluth, D. & Bowlby, J. (1952) *A two-year-old goes to hospital*. In: *Psychoanalytic study of the child*, New York, International Universities Press, Vol. 7, p. 82

53. Roudinesco J. & Appell, G. (1950) Les répercussions de la stabilisation hospitalière sur le développement psycho-moteur de jeunes enfants. *Sem. Hôp. Paris*, **26**, 2271

54. Scott, J. P., Fredericson, E. & Fuller, J. L. (1951) Experimental exploration of the critical period hypothesis. *Personality*, **1**, 162

55. Scott, J. P. & Marston, M. V. (1950) Critical periods affecting the development of normal and maladjustive social behaviour of puppies. *J. genet. Psychol.*, **77**, 25

56. Spitz, R. A. (1945) *Hospitalism*. In: *Psychoanalytic study of the child*, New York, International Universities Press, Vol. 1, p. 53

57. Spitz, R. A. (1959) *La première année de la vie de l'enfant*, Paris, Presses universitaires de France

58. Spitz, R. A. & Wolf, K. (1946) *Anaclitic depression*. In: *Psychoanalytic study of the child*, New York, International Universities Press, Vol. 2, p. 313

59. Taylor, F. Kräupl (1958) [Letter to the Editor]. *Lancet*, **1**, 643

60. Tinbergen, N. (1951) *The study of instinct*, Oxford, Clarendon Press

THE EFFECTS OF MATERNAL DEPRIVATION: A REVIEW OF FINDINGS AND CONTROVERSY IN THE CONTEXT OF RESEARCH STRATEGY

MARY D. AINSWORTH *

During the fifteen years preceding the appearance of Bowlby's *Maternal Care and Mental Health*,[16] studies by Levy, Skeels and his associates, Burlingham & Freud, Bowlby, Bender, Goldfarb, Spitz and many others bore witness to the adverse effects of early deprivation of maternal care. Bowlby, in 1951, introduced his timely review of the research evidence by saying:

> " The extent to which these studies, undertaken by people of many nations, varied training and, as often as not, ignorant of each others' conclusions, confirm and support each other is impressive. What each individual piece of work lacks in thoroughness, scientific reliability, or precision is largely made good by the concordance of the whole " (p. 15).[16]

Moreover, in reviewing the expert opinion of those responsible for planning for the care of " homeless " children, Bowlby again found impressive agreement. In organizing this mass of opinion and evidence to make it widely available to all of those concerned with child development and child care, Bowlby became the eloquent spokesman for a point of view that not only offered a guide for the immediate improvement of child care, but also provided an impetus for further research of a more rigorous quality. Major points needing investigation were, for example, the relationships between the age of the child, the duration and the severity of deprivation and the resulting effects of deprivation. Furthermore, although the damaging effects of severe, early and prolonged deprivation had been clearly established, the processes through which deprivation worked its damage were not. A more adequate understanding was needed of the role played by early interpersonal interaction in shaping the subsequent development of the child.

As the contributors to this volume testify, a great body of productive research has followed the strong stimulus of Bowlby's monograph.

---

* Department of Psychology, Johns Hopkins University, Baltimore, Md., USA.

These last ten years of activity have clearly shown that research into the effects of maternal deprivation is extremely difficult and complex, and that the problems and findings are not as simple as they may have seemed to the reader of *Maternal Care and Mental Health* in 1951. This complexity is reflected in the divergent emphases of the contributors to this volume, and in the varied and sometimes conflicting findings and opinions of the authors quoted by them. This chapter will therefore consider, in the light of the pertinent research evidence of the past ten years, the main controversial questions raised by the other contributors to this volume.

THE CHIEF CONTROVERSIAL QUESTIONS

The controversy in the field of maternal deprivation is much more a controversy of opinion than of research facts. Indeed, the research findings, when viewed in perspective, form a complex but coherent body of interlocking facts that has many gaps but no inherent contradictions. Nevertheless several points have been raised as controversial which it is hoped that this chapter will help to clarify. In an attempt to dispel apparent confusion, therefore, nine controversial questions will now be discussed.

The question of definition of maternal deprivation

The term " maternal deprivation " has been applied to different sets of conditions, which, singly or in combination, sometimes appear to have similar consequences. The three major sets of conditions which have been explored in research are: (*a*) deprivation that occurs when an infant or young child lives in an institution or hospital where he has no major substitute mother, where he receives insufficient maternal care, and consequently has insufficient opportunity for interaction with a mother-figure; (*b*) deprivation that occurs when an infant or young child lives with his mother or permanent substitute mother, from whom he receives insufficient care and with whom he has insufficient interaction; (*c*) deprivation that comes about through the child's own inability to interact with a mother-figure despite the fact that one is present and ready to give sufficient care—this inability to interact being consequent on and presumably caused by repeated breaches of ties with mother-figures (or, of course, previous deprivation experiences). In all of these conditions, the implicit definition of maternal deprivation is insufficiency of interaction between the child and a mother-figure.

Mother-child separation also has been subsumed frequently under the term " maternal deprivation ". If deprivation is defined as insufficiency of interaction, it does not follow that separation necessarily implies deprivation. Mother-child separation may provide the occasion for deprivation if the child then goes to a setting, institutional or otherwise, where he has insufficient interaction with a substitute mother, or if the separation experience is oft repeated. It is not yet known how many repetitions of separation experiences are needed to bring about deprivation, or under what conditions a sequence of separations leads to this outcome. A single separation experience, however, need not be depriving—not if the child is offered a major substitute figure with whom he can sufficiently interact. Nevertheless, a non-depriving separation experience can be distressing to a child old enough to discriminate his mother from other persons and to have formed an attachment to her, yet not old enough to maintain this attachment while parted from her. It seems desirable to reserve the term " mother-child separation " for discontinuities in a relationship once formed, rather than to apply it more widely to cover all instances of parting the child from his mother, regardless of the age of the child or the nature of the attachment between them and its degree of maturity. Because of the distress they bring, discontinuities in attachments may have adverse effects on development, but these effects are not necessarily the same as the effects of deprivation, unless, as often happens, the separation leads to a deprivation experience.

The term " maternal deprivation " has been used also to cover nearly every undesirable kind of interaction between mother and child—rejection, hostility, cruelty, over-indulgence, repressive control, lack of affection and the like. A term used to cover all pathogenic variations of mother-child relations is too inclusive and hence confusing. It is therefore suggested that the term " distorted " be applied to social transactions of an adverse character, and that the term " depriving " be reserved for interactions of insufficient quantity, without reference to their character.

The complexity of antecedent conditions that have been subsumed under the term " maternal deprivation " has been an understandable source of confusion to many. If confusion and consequent controversy is to be avoided, distinctions should be maintained between the following: (a) insufficiency of interaction implicit in deprivation; (b) distortion in the character of the interaction, without respect to its quantity; and (c) the discontinuity of relations brought about through separation. These distinctions will be maintained throughout this paper, although all three dimensions of mother-child interaction—insufficiency, distortion and discontinuity—will be discussed, because they have all been included by loose custom under the term " maternal deprivation ".

The question of " multiple mothers "

Bowlby's emphasis on the desirability of continuity in the relations between the child and his mother (or substitute mother) and on the importance of a quantity of interaction sufficient for him to be able to form an attachment to this figure has been interpreted by some (for example, by Mead in her contribution to this volume (see page 45)) to imply that Bowlby believes that any dispersion of maternal care among a number of figures has an adverse effect. Perhaps no one would deny the value of continuity in whatever mothering arrangements are made for the care of a child. To say that continuity is needed, however, does not imply that an exclusive mother-child pair-relationship is essential if deprivation is to be avoided.* Bowlby himself [21] has acknowledged the desirability of supplementing the care given by the mother with care from other figures. Nevertheless, the notion that multiplicity of mother-figures brings about deprivation has become both widespread and controversial.

The question of variability in the degree of damage following deprivation

Maternal deprivation in infancy and early childhood has been found to result in varying degrees of impairment. Some of the variation in degree of damage may be explained by differences in the severity of the deprivation experiences themselves. Some of the disparity between studies with respect to degree of damage is an artefact of the level of observation employed. Not all damage is sufficiently gross to be obvious at a crude level of observation. Often enough appreciable damage can be detected only at the more refined level of observation provided by quantitative tests, clinical appraisal techniques or other well-controlled observations of behaviour. For example, a group of deprived children may be found significantly inferior to non-deprived children in language ability when standardized tests of language are used, although their inferiority may not be apparent merely from listening to their talk. Even when careful appraisal is undertaken, however, some deprived children are found to be more adversely affected than

---

* Although in the earliest months of life it is the mother who almost invariably interacts most with the child, and to whom the child usually displays his first attachment, the role of other figures, especially the father, is acknowledged to be significant. While maternal deprivation has preoccupied investigators for the past twenty-five years, paternal deprivation, as Andry points out in this volume (see page 31), has received scant attention. Moreover, in many instances where the term " maternal deprivation " has been used—for example, in institutionalization—the term " parental deprivation " would have been more accurate, for the child has been parted from both parents and deprived of interaction with a father-figure as well as with a mother-figure. Although this neglect of the father is to be deplored, the present review will continue to neglect him; there is more than enough material on maternal deprivation alone to occupy one review. It is to be hoped that future research will give more adequate attention to the influence of father-child interaction on the course of development. In the meantime, perhaps, this chapter, in helping to clarify the misunderstandings that have arisen with respect to maternal deprivation, will prevent similar misunderstandings about paternal deprivation from arising, or, better still, will discourage the use of the term " paternal deprivation", and encourage the substitution of the terms " insufficiency ", " discontinuity ", and " distortion " instead.

others, while some emerge with little or no apparent damage. The fact that some seem to escape unscathed has led some critics to question the validity of the proposition that maternal deprivation is pathogenic.

When other sources of variability in degree of damage have been ruled out, the variability that remains is usually attributed to individual differences in vulnerability, and these in turn are attributed either to differences in genetic constitution or to differences in environmental influences upon development prior to the onset of deprivation or to both. Differences in vulnerability are commonly found in etiological research, even when the pathogenic agent has been established beyond doubt. These differences, in themselves, do not constitute sufficient grounds either for judging an etiological hypothesis to be invalid or for opposing preventive measures stemming from the hypothesis.

The question of specific versus general effects of deprivation

Maternal deprivation has a differential effect on different processes. Although prolonged and very severe deprivation during infancy may at the time affect so many processes that the child seems totally impaired, even then, upon close examination, some processes are found to be more severely affected than others. (The age of the child at the time of the onset of deprivation seems to be important in determining what processes are impaired and to what degree.) Researches that differ with respect to the processes examined will inevitably yield disparate findings. Thus, one study may examine general intelligence, another language ability, another the character of interpersonal attachments, and yet another habit disorders such as thumb-sucking and bed-wetting; yet some critics have concluded that, if deprivation results in no adverse effect on the particular process studied, no damage has been done to the other processes which have not been examined. The unjustified assumption that deprivation affects all processes in equal degree has been a major source of misunderstanding and hence of controversy.

The question of diversity in the nature of the adverse effects of deprivation

The effects of maternal deprivation have been found to be diverse in nature as well as in degree. Some of these diversities obviously can be explained by the great diversity of antecedent experiences that have been subsumed under the term " maternal deprivation ". But even the same class of deprivation experience affecting the same process (although perhaps with different degrees of severity) may result in disparate overt outcomes in different children. Thus, for example, the processes through which interpersonal ties are established and maintained may be affected, but one child may emerge as detached and

" affectionless ", while another may cling anxiously to his mother and seem over-dependent on her. The paradoxical nature of the diversity of outcomes has led some critics to be sceptical that they could stem from the same cause.

The question of permanence of the effects of deprivation

The claim made by Bowlby, Spitz and others that severe, early deprivation of maternal care may have permanent effects has led to controversy. Some critics, who acknowledge that young children are impaired while undergoing deprivation, are reluctant to concede that any early experience can lead to permanent residual impairment that cannot be eliminated through favourable influences later in life. This controversy has been facilitated by several considerations of which the most important seem to be: (a) even a severely damaged child may improve to some extent if deprivation is relieved; (b) impairment of some processes seems more resistant to reversal than impairment of other processes; (c) some damage is more obvious and more easily observable than other damage that may nevertheless be more resistant to reversal; and, finally (d) it is very likely that some lasting effects are manifested overtly only under special circumstances—perhaps much later in life—which reactivate pathological processes originally set in train by the early deprivation experience. Inadequate attention to these considerations has led some critics to be convinced that early deprivation cannot be the cause of later pathology.

The special question of delinquency

Particular controversy has centred upon delinquency as an outcome of maternal deprivation. Bender & Yarnell [12] applied the term " psychopathic behaviour disorder " to the clinical syndrome they found associated with early severe deprivation experiences. An early study of Bowlby's [15] used juvenile thieves as subjects, and demonstrated an association between the " affectionless character " shown by some of these thieves and early, severely depriving separation experiences. Bowlby suggested that separation experiences of this nature may be foremost among the causes of " delinquent character formation ". These, and similar findings and opinions of other early investigators, have led to the widely held belief that the hypothesis of maternal deprivation as pathogenic necessarily implies that deprivation causes delinquency. The fact that delinquency has not been found to be a *common* outcome of maternal deprivation and that early mother-child separation is not a consistent antecedent in groups of delinquents have therefore seemed to some critics to disprove the hypothesis of the pathogenicity of deprivation.

The question of " maternal" versus " environmental" deprivation

Among those who accept the evidence that institutional care of infants and young children is generally depriving there is controversy about whether the deprivation is attributable to the absence of a mother-figure or to " environmental deprivation " contingent upon a relatively low level of stimulation in the institution setting. This controversy seems due in part to a protest against any tendency to ascribe mystic properties to the care given to the child by his natural mother and in part to a desire to understand deprivation in terms compatible with stimulus-response theory.

Minor controversial questions

Finally, there are minor controversial questions, such as the place of defective genetic constitution in contributing to the retardation of young children in institutions or to the frequency of undiagnosed organic brain damage in cases of infants manifesting a " hospitalism " syndrome.

This chapter will consider these nine points of controversy in the light of the research evidence, giving attention both to the interacting variables operating in the deprivation experiences studied and to the research strategy and methods of data collection used; in this context, there seem to be no serious contradictions between studies. Our knowledge of the effects of maternal deprivation to date will be seen to be a remarkably coherent body of knowledge—with many gaps and open-ended questions, to be sure—but with no implicit controversy. Moreover, there will be seen to be no serious contradiction between the findings as reviewed by Bowlby and the interim conclusions he drew from them in 1951 and our present knowledge of the effects of maternal deprivation. His major and most quoted statement is not challenged by recent findings: " It is submitted that the evidence is now such that it leaves no room for doubt regarding the general proposition—that the *prolonged* deprivation of the *young* child of maternal care *may* have grave and far-reaching effects on his character and so on the whole of his future life " (p. 46; my italics). [16]

REASONS FOR CONTROVERSY

Some controversy seems due entirely to misunderstanding, over-simplification or distortion of the findings and conclusions of earlier work. Thus, to illustrate with only one example, Andry in his contribution to this volume (see page 31) states: "The concept of 'maternal deprivation', as brought out clearly by Dr John Bowlby, seems to

imply that one of the most dangerous pathogenic factors in child development is the harm that may be done if a child has been deprived of his
natural mother's love through separation ". Andry ignores two of the
three important qualifying words italicized in the above quotation from
Bowlby. Furthermore, he distorts Bowlby's oft-repeated term " mother
(or permanent mother-substitute) " into " natural mother ". He implies
that Bowlby believes maternal deprivation to be limited to instances of
separation, and that Bowlby pays no heed to other aspects of maternal
deprivation that may accompany the separation experience.

Secondly, some unnecessary controversy stems from inadequate
recognition that both " maternal deprivation " and " mother-child
separation " are terms that cover many kinds of experience, differing
greatly in severity, and that the effects of these experiences depend on a
multiplicity of variables, including the age of the child at the onset of
deprivation, the nature of his experiences before this onset, the duration
of the deprivation, and the nature of his experiences after deprivation
has been relieved. Ainsworth & Bowlby [2] discussed in some detail the
many factors which play a part in influencing the outcome of mother-
child separation, and by extension similar influences may be assumed
to have significance in maternal deprivation in the absence of separation.
Although in this volume Lebovici, Andry, and Prugh & Harlow have
all acknowledged the importance of these variables, it is impossible to
give them too much stress. Many seeming inconsistencies between
studies are due to disregarding these sources of variance, either when
planning the study or when interpreting the findings or both.

Thirdly, some of the controversy seems due to an erroneous belief
that a single complex of experiences, more or less prolonged, occurring
in early childhood will have a uniform and lasting effect in all cases.
Development of the individual organism is an unbroken process. A
deprivation experience acts through its influence upon on-going processes and is interpreted in the light of previous experience. The on-
going processes upon which it acts are, in turn, a result of the whole
previous history of development that has taken place through the
interaction of the organism (and its genetically determined structure)
with environmental influences. The response to relief from deprivation
is determined both by the processes set up in the course of the deprivation experience and by the extent to which they are reinforced, modified
or reversed by later organism-environment interactions. All of these
influences are important in determining the eventual outcome. Indeed,
a vicious spiral exacerbating the effects of a severe deprivation experience
is not uncommon: the processes set up by deprivation make it difficult
for a child to respond adequately to the later advances of a mother-
figure; the mother, in turn, tends to interact less with the child than she

would have done with a more responsive child, or perhaps to reject him; in this way, a mother may unknowingly reinforce the processes set up in the original deprivation experience. Similarly, a child who has been damaged by deprivation experiences at home before admission to an institution may be more neglected in the institution than a more responsive child. But to find that pre-separation and post-separation experiences influence the effect of separation is not to say that the depriving separation experience itself had a negligible influence on the outcome.

Finally, some of the controversy seems to stem from the complex and difficult problems implicit in research into the effect of maternal deprivation. Various research strategies are available, each with its own strengths and deficiencies, which set limits on the kind of findings and interpretations each can yield. The inappropriate use of a strategy, therefore, can lead to findings that are seemingly contradictory to the main body of knowledge. Problems of research strategy were considered at length by Ainsworth & Bowlby [2] and will be discussed more briefly here.

THE FINDINGS IN THE CONTEXT OF RESEARCH STRATEGY

The experimental method, the backbone of laboratory research, has limited applicability to the study of maternal deprivation. Once the hypothesis had been put forward that prolonged deprivation experiences in early childhood may have lasting adverse effects upon subsequent development, it was out of the question to expose young children experimentally to deprivation in order to test the hypothesis. Consequently, research into the effects of maternal deprivation cannot avail itself of the great advantage of the experimental method—namely, precise control of the conditions the effect of which is to be studied. Thus, it is impossible to arrange a depriving situation of a controlled nature and degree of severity, into which a child may be introduced at a given age and kept for a pre-determined time. Since the depriving conditions cannot be controlled through experimental manipulation, they must be controlled through selection—that is, by choosing for study a deprived group who happen to experience deprivation under certain defined conditions. It is impossible to overemphasize the importance of control of conditions through careful selection if other than equivocal results are to be obtained.

Research into the effects of maternal deprivation differs from laboratory experimentation also in regard to the time span of the study. Laboratory experimentation is usually concerned with effects that immediately follow the experimental treatment, and part of the excellence of control implicit in experiment is control throughout the whole period from the onset of the " treatment " to the final observation of " effect ". On the other hand, etiological research, especially in the field of personality development, covers a relatively long span of time, sometimes many years, between antecedent and effect, through a period in which conditions are uncontrolled. Meanwhile life goes on. Longitudinal research deals with the very stuff of life and human development, with all its consequent complexities and difficulties. Several important considerations follow. First, an antecedent experience must be very profound to leave gross and obvious traces of cause-and-effect relationships after the lapse of years filled with many other influences. Secondly, significant effects may be present that are not grossly observable, and, therefore, the most sensitive available methods should be used to assess the effects. Unfortunately, there is still a woeful lack of precise and reliable measuring devices available for the assessment of many effects that have been attributed to maternal deprivation. Some investigators have met this challenge and devised ways of quantifying the appropriate observations, [69], [93] but others have seemed to choose techniques merely because they were available and quantitative and not because they were appropriate to the problems.[85]

Because of the need to use careful methods to observe the variables and to assess the effects, research in the field of maternal deprivation is time-consuming. It is no field for rapid research in which large-scale techniques can be used. Indeed, the nature of the appropriate techniques demands small rather than large samples, and the cause-effect picture can be built up only gradually through many such small samples studied under different conditions, rather than through any large and final hypothesis testing.

Ainsworth & Bowlby [2] have considered four major research strategies that are being used in the field of maternal deprivation. Of these, retrospective case studies, retrospective follow-up studies and current studies will be considered here. Psychoanalytic research studies also constitute a significant strategy, but since they are still more projected than finished research, they will be omitted here. Two additional methods—believed by Ainsworth & Bowlby to have only limited applicability for the study of the effects of maternal deprivation—have been used by recent investigators. Hence, the population study and the experimental study will also be discussed here.

Retrospective case studies

The retrospective case study strategy is invaluable in etiological research as a means of formulating hypotheses. This strategy is characterized by the identification of a syndrome, or cluster of related symptoms or personality characteristics, and by the exploration of the history of the patient or patients displaying this syndrome to discover likely antecedents that might account for the outcome. Retrospective case studies vary from studies of a few cases which suggest that a certain kind of outcome might be causally related to a specific antecedent condition, to studies in which formal statistical tests are made of the extent to which the antecedent condition does in fact differentiate between those who display the syndrome and a control group of subjects who do not. The characteristics of the retrospective case study strategy will be illustrated by two early examples.

Bender, [11, 12] in a study of children admitted to hospital for psychiatric observation or treatment, identified a syndrome labelled " psychopathic behaviour disorder " and described the functions affected in such careful detail that she greatly facilitated the work of later investigators in testing her hypothesis. Thus, for example, she specified defects in language, abstract function, and conceptualization of time as part of the syndrome, as well as impairment in capacity for close affectional ties (and these particulars and others have been confirmed by subsequent studies that have made assessments careful enough to take note of these features). The antecedent condition was identified as severe and early maternal deprivation, and it too was carefully delineated. Even in this early study the three major patterns of severe deprivation were identified—prolonged depriving institutional experience, repeated breaches of ties with mother-figures, and severely depriving relations with parents in the absence of separation—and special significance was attached to deprivation in the first two or three years of life.

Bowlby's study[15] dealt with juvenile thieves and a control group of non-thieves both drawn from the population of a child guidance clinic. He also began with the identification of a syndrome, the " affectionless character ", which closely resembled Bender's " psychopathic behaviour disorder ". Bowlby's study was more systematic, in that he employed statistical tests of the differences in incidence of the antecedent condition hypothesized as cause between the juvenile thieves who showed this syndrome, the other thieves, and the control group of non-thieves. His identification of the antecedent condition was also much the same as Bender's, but in his final, much-quoted summing up, he neglected to make clear that the pathogenic antecedent hypothesized to be the cause of the affectionless character was not simply early prolonged separation, but separation either with deprivation of sufficient maternal care, or, more frequently in his sample, with deprivation brought about by repeated shifts of mother-figures; this omission has led to some misunderstanding.

Using these two classic studies as examples, three main features of the productive, hypothesis-producing, research-provoking case study may be distinguished: (a) thorough clinical assessment as a basis for identifying the syndrome or " effect "; (b) clinical exploration of the history to identify and specify in detail the antecedent conditions hypothesized to be causally related to the " effect "; and (c) flexibility in delineating the antecedents in terms of the particular sample studied. This flexible feature is both a great strength, in that it enables the investigator to specify his hypothesized antecedent with some precision, and a great weakness, in that it leads readily to the *post hoc ergo propter hoc* fallacy. Thus it is easy but fallacious to jump from the observation that psychopathic or affectionless characters in a clinical setting commonly have experienced severe, prolonged and early maternal deprivation to the conviction that severe, early and prolonged maternal deprivation commonly produces psychopathic or affectionless characters.

" *Deprivation* " *with and without separation.*   During the last ten years retrospective case studies have continued to contribute to an understanding of the effects of maternal deprivation.   One significant mass of evidence and opinion emphasizes that " deprivation " can occur at home in the absence of mother-child separation.   Prugh & Harlow, in their contribution to the present volume (see page 9), submit unsystematic case study evidence in support of their hypothesis that " masked deprivation " in the absence of physical separation can be associated with outcomes as pathological as those that follow severely depriving separation experiences.   They distinguish two kinds of " masked deprivation "—" insufficient " relatedness between the child and his parents, and particularly the mother, and " distorted " relatedness.   Thus, by implication, they identify the three dimensions—insufficiency, distortion and discontinuity—which have been advanced in this chapter as a basis for classifying pathogenic mother-child interactions.   Having made the distinction, however, they proceed to consider all these kinds of pathogenic interactions as instances of " deprivation "; perhaps because of this they despair of the possibility of identifying the specific patterns of antecedent conditions that lead to specific outcomes.

One important feature of Prugh & Harlow's contribution is to correct the widespread misconception that the so-called " maternal deprivation theorists " concern themselves only with the effects of deprivation associated with mother-child separation, and ignore deprivation that may occur through insufficient interaction between the child and his mother at home.   As Prugh & Harlow themselves acknowledge, Bowlby, having been assigned the task of exploring the plight of " homeless " children, restricted his review to deprivation contingent upon separation. Bowlby [16] specifically stated that he was leaving out of consideration " partial " deprivation occurring without separation—although in an earlier publication,[14] he considered various types of early childhood experience ₁which were associated with pathological outcomes, and included insufficient and distorted mother-child interaction as well as separation.

If early pathogenic mother-child relations are described in terms of insufficiency, discontinuity and distortion, the terms " masked " or " partial " deprivation become superfluous. " Deprivation " then refers to insufficiency of mother-child interaction, whether correlated with discontinuity or distortion or not. " Separation " refers to discontinuity in a relationship, whether occurring with insufficiency or distortion or not. The term " distorted interaction " includes various patterns of interaction believed to have an adverse effect on the subsequent development of the child, without reference to the quantity or continuity of the interaction. Obviously all three variables may be pertinent to the description of an individual case. For example, a child having had both insufficient and distorted interaction with a rejecting mother, then may be separated from her and placed in an institution where he experiences insufficient interaction with a substitute mother, because he is cared for by many persons, no one of whom is primarily responsible for him and all of whom together give insufficient care. The confounding of variables that may occur in the invidiual case makes it difficult to sort out the effect of any one variable in isolation. This sorting out of associations between specific antecedents and specific effects can, however, be accomplished through studies in which different clusters of antecedents are represented in the sample of cases, but sorting out can only be achieved if the distinctions between insufficiency, discontinuity and distortion are kept clearly in mind.

A study by Howells & Layng [73] clearly illustrates the misconceptions that have arisen through failure to distinguish between insufficiency, discontinuity and distortion in mother-child interaction as significant antecedents of subsequent pathology. Howells & Layng, assuming that Bowlby hypothesized early mother-child *separation*—whether involving *deprivation* or not—to be a significant antecedent of all kinds of psychiatric disorders in children, compared a group of child guidance clinic cases (without distinguishing the types of disorder displayed) with a control group of schoolchildren, in regard to separations of the child from either the mother or the father or both before the age of five years. They considered all separations, however brief, and found no appreciable differences between the groups, except for separations over three months in duration which occurred in only one of the controls and in six of the clinic cases. They concluded that poor mental health arises from processes stemming from faulty interaction with parents rather than from being away from them, and that Bowlby's review [16] concerned children who were suffering from deprivation rather than from separation *per se*. To imply that Bowlby hypothesized that early separation was a significant antecedent in all kinds of disturbance, that he ignored the fact that it is in combination with deprivation that separation is most pathogenic, and that he belittled distortions in parent-child relations as antecedents of personality disturbances, are all serious misinterpretations of his position and of his supporting evidence.

From a research point of view, there were good reasons for Bowlby and others to focus on deprivation contingent upon separation, and especially on institutional experience, because the relevant conditions which define the severity of the deprivation are much more easily identified and assessed than in the case of deprivation occurring without actual separation. The difficulties of research into deprivation *with* separation are great; the difficulties of research into deprivation *without* separation are formidable indeed.

Paradoxically, much of the evidence pointing to the pathogenic influence of insufficient or distorted but continuous mother-child interaction comes from retrospective studies of persons who were later separated—studies which suggest that the character and quantity of the interaction experienced in pre-separation relationships with parents is important in influencing either the state of the child at the time of separation or his subsequent development or both. Indeed, some of these studies suggest that pre-separation interaction may be so severely depriving or distorting that life in a good institution can represent considerable relief. Thus Clarke & Clarke [35-38] report that certified feeble-minded patients who made substantial gains in IQ over a period of years in an institution significantly more frequently had come from " exceptionally adverse homes " than those who made less substantial gains or none. Unfortunately, since the Clarkes did not specify the nature of the early parent-child relations that made the early experiences " exceptionally adverse ", the specific etiology of the severe intellectual impairment is unknown.

Lewis [78] also focused on pathogenic pre-separation experiences. Her complex study dealt with 500 children admitted to a reception centre, some of whom had had insufficient parent-child interaction, some distorted relations, some discontinuous relations because of earlier separation, and others a combination of these conditions. The children were classified according to the degree of disturbance in their mental state and according to the qualitative patterns of behaviour manifest at the time of admission, and then their case histories were searched to find what features of their previous experience might be associated statistically with their current states and patterns. Lasting separation of the child from the mother before the age of two was one of seven features of early parent-child relations that was significantly and positively related to the degree of maladjustment; the other features were lack of maternal affection, maternal over-indulgence, maternal mental illness, paternal neglect, paternal over-indulgence, and prolonged public care. Thus this study provides a further piece of evidence that deprivation, distortion, or discontinuity in mother-child relations—singly or in combination—can all be antecedents of adverse outcomes and suggests that insufficiency or distortion in father-child interaction can also be pathogenic.

Lewis's study also yields some hypotheses about the specific antecedents of certain patterns of disturbed behaviour. Thus parental rejection seemed a significant antecedent to " unsocialized aggression ", neglect by parents tended to precede " socialized delinquency ", while a " repressive regimen " seemed associated with later neurotic adjustment. Lasting separation was not, however, an antecedent of any particular pattern of disturbance. A " repressive regimen " implies distortion rather than insufficiency in parent-child interaction; parental neglect seems to imply insufficiency, although distortion may also enter in; rejection, on the other hand, primarily implies distortion, although insufficiency of interaction may follow. Although Prugh & Harlow offer a counsel of despair about the likelihood of finding any specific personality configuration as an outcome of any specific antecedent condition, Lewis's findings suggest a more hopeful prospect.

Wootton (in her study, *Social Science and Social Pathology*,[127] and in this volume (see page 64)) and others have given major emphasis to those aspects of Lewis's findings that pertain to mother-child separation. Although lasting separation before the age of two was found to be related significantly to a disturbed mental state, it was not related to any specific personality pattern. Furthermore, neither temporary separations of three months or more nor lasting separations after the age of two seemed to be related significantly to the degree or nature of maladjustment. Wootton and others have interpreted these findings to demonstrate the insignificance of separation as a pathogenic agent. The nature of the control group should be borne in mind here, however; although the comparison was with non-separated controls, most of them undoubtedly could be characterized as having had insufficient or distorted parent-child relations. Further, the exploration of the histories stressed the quality of the disturbance of parent-child relations, and did not assess its severity; even with respect to separation it is not known, for example, how many children had had adequate substitute mothering. Moreover, it seems likely that the three variables—insufficiency, distortion and discontinuity—were so confounded in these cases that the study does not permit a conclusion to be drawn about the nature

and degree of the antecedent experiences that led to the most pathological outcomes.

*Factors influencing degree of impairment resulting from depriving
separation experiences.* Once it is recognized that varying degrees of
impairment may result from deprivation, the question immediately
becomes one of identifying the antecedent conditions that influence
degree of damage. Trasler [123] and Kellmer Pringle & Bossio [88] provide
evidence about the factors influencing the degree of impairment attributable to depriving separation experiences.

Trasler [123] dealt entirely with separated children in foster-homes,
comparing a group of children unsuccessfully placed (i.e., with at least
one failure in a foster-home, leading to re-placement, whatever the
ostensible reason for the failure) with a group that had been successfully placed. He explored both the antecedent histories and the present
situation of each child, relying chiefly upon formal reports and informal
communication from the case workers responsible for the cases. He
found that 56 % of the failures in foster-homes were primarily or
secondarily due to the effects on the child of separation from his
parents—effects attributable to feelings of rejection (whether real or
imagined) which generated tension, anxiety and inhibition of responsiveness to the foster-parents. That the children were " isolated "
or affectionless, and unable to respond to the overtures of the foster-
parents accounted, at least partially, for 30% of the failures. Relatively
few failures were attributable either to the intellectual retardation of
the child or to inadequacies of the foster-parents. Prolonged institutional care during the earliest years of life, occurring after separation from the parents and before placement with the foster-parents,
was the antecedent condition most significantly associated with subsequent failure in the foster-home. Affectionless detachment or " isolation ", feelings of rejection and consequent aggression seemed most
likely to develop if institutional placement intervened between parent-
child separation and placement in a foster-home. The successful foster-
home placements tended to be those made before four years of age with
a minimum of institutional care intervening between separation and
placement.   Trasler concluded that young children tend to interpret
separation from their parents as the withdrawal of affection, and that
this causes difficulty in subsequent adjustment to caretakers. For the
child under three years of age, the disturbance attributable to separation
can be mild and transitory if the child is provided with the opportunity
of interaction with an individual mother-figure, but the disturbance
tends to be more severe and lasting if he experiences the insufficient
interaction characteristic of institutional care.

Kellmer Pringle & Bossio [88] selected, from among institution children who had undergone prolonged separation from their parents before five years of age, a group of eleven judged by all criteria to be severely maladjusted and a group of five judged notably stable. They used the retrospective case study approach to determine what antecedent conditions distinguished the groups from each other. Age at separation seemed important, since nine of the severely maladjusted children had been first separated before twelve months of age, while four of the five stable children had been at least two years old when first separated. Moreover, the separations of the severely maladjusted group seemed to have been accompanied by lasting parental rejection, and these children had since lacked either the opportunity or the ability to establish any stable relations with parent-substitutes. In contrast, the stable children, though separated, had not been rejected by parents, and had maintained a lasting relationship with either parents or parent-substitutes. In summary, this study, as well as Trasler's, suggests that the most severe impairment occurs when very young children are separated from their parents and placed in an institutional environment where they have no opportunity for sufficient interaction with a parent-figure; the institutional experience, moreover, fosters a feeling of having been rejected by the parents and thus hampers the child's future responsiveness to new parent-figures.

Diverse and sometimes " hidden " consequences of severe separation. Separation experiences in early childhood may be classed as " severe " for several reasons: because they usher in a prolonged period of deprivation, because the separation itself is particularly traumatic, or because the loss of the parent is permanent. Sometimes, when the circumstances of substitute care are not known, the mere fact that the separation was prolonged may be grounds for classing the experience as " severe ". This was the case in a study by Earle & Earle,[47] who found among 1423 psychiatric patients 100 who had suffered mother-child separation for at least six months before the age of six years. This separated group included patients with varied diagnoses, but they showed a significantly higher prevalence of sociopathic personality disturbances and childhood behaviour disorders than a control group of patients. Among the separated group the prevalence of sociopathic personality was 27% while in the remaining 1323 patients it was 2.9%. Thus, although there was a diversity of outcomes among the separated patients, nevertheless there seemed to be a special link between separation and a sociopathic outcome.

Earle & Earle found depressive illness to be more frequent in the control group than in the separated group, but in the separated group itself depression was significantly more frequent among those who had lost their mothers through death than among those whose separation had had other causes. Other studies have devoted themselves specifically to childhood bereavement. (It may be noted that when bereavement is studied rather than other types of separation experience the control group can be the general population as a whole, as represented by census figures or actuarial tables.) Barry [9] found that the loss of the mother through death, either in the first five or in the second five years of life, was an antecedent occurrence significantly more frequent among mental hospital patients than in the general population. The loss of the father through death was also an antecedent significantly more frequent among mental hospital patients than in the general population; here, however, the important childhood period was from five to ten years. Barry & Lindemann [10] found that loss of the mother through death before the age of five years was significantly more frequent among out-patients suffering from psychoneurotic or psychosomatic disorders than in a control group, whereas loss of the mother at older ages or loss of the father at any age (before sixteen) was not more frequent in the patient group. Brown [31] devoted himself to a study of depressive patients; he found that loss of the mother through death in each of the five-year periods from birth to fifteen years of age was significantly more frequent among the depressive group than in the general population; and that the loss of the father through death between the ages of five and fifteen was also significantly more frequent among the depressives.

Bowlby attaches particular significance to studies reporting an association between childhood bereavement and depressive illness because of the similarity he has observed between grief and mourning in the adult and the " despair " phase of response to separation in the young child. Furthermore, he hypothesizes that the defensive detachment which succeeds despair, if the young child suffers a depriving separation for a prolonged period, precludes a healthy working through of grief, and predisposes him to later depressive reactions. Bowlby developed the theoretical foundations for this hypothesis in a series of papers. [24, 26, 27] The link between early bereavement and subsequent depressive reaction suggests that a predisposition to depressive illness may be one of the hidden effects of prolonged and severe separation experiences in early childhood, one which may well escape notice until some later precipitating situation touches off the latent pathology. In general these retrospective case studies, especially those by Lewis, Earle & Earle, and Brown, suggest the worth of further case studies specifically designed to formulate etiological hypotheses linking specific outcomes to specific types and degrees of disturbance of early parent-child interaction.

Specific processes affected by deprivation. In connexion with the specific processes particularly affected by early deprivation experiences, Bender's contribution has already been mentioned. Among the more recent studies, that of Trasler [123] provides further evidence. His findings highlighted the specific vulnerability to deprivation of the processes through which the child is able to interact deeply and intimately with a parent-figure. Williams, [126] like Trasler, was chiefly concerned with children whose foster-home placements had failed. She confined herself to children between the ages of five and eleven who had to be removed from foster-homes because of unsatisfactory relations between the child and his foster-parents rather than because the foster-home itself was of poor quality. Williams' children (who, on the basis of Trasler's evidence, may be assumed to have been severely deprived) were compared with a control group of family-reared children who had recently been separated from their parents for a temporary stay in a reception centre. Williams found that 80% of the " breakdown " group (i.e., those who had failed to adjust in foster-homes and has had to be re-placed) had been first separated from their mothers before the age of two years. She reported that these children's language function was specifically affected, since they had significantly lower verbal than performance IQs on the Wechsler Intelligence Test for Children. The differences that emerged through the use of the Rorschach, Children's Apperception Test and Bene-Anthony Family Relations Test may be summarized as follows: in contrast with the control group the deprived children (i.e., the break-down group) tended at first to be uninhibited and impulsive, but by seven years of age appeared to be defensive and limited; they tended to feel punished, rejected and deserted by parents, and lonely and confused; they tended to deny normal dependency feelings, massively to repress aggressive feelings and grossly to lack self-regard.

Delinquency and separation. The link found by Earle & Earle [47] between separation and sociopathic disorders is reminiscent of the link found by Bowlby [15] between early, severe separation experiences and " affectionless " thieves. Bowlby's conclusion that early and severe or oft-repeated separation experiences may be a " foremost cause of delinquent character formation " has led to considerable controversy. Studies by Glueck & Glueck [53] and Wardle [124] tend to support Bowlby's hypothesis, while studies by Andry [3] and Naess [84] do not.

Glueck & Glueck [63] found that loss, before a child's fifth birthday, of either parent through death, divorce, separation or prolonged absence was an antecedent condition twice as frequent in a delinquent group as in a matched group of non-delinquents ($p < 0.001$). Similar loss occurring between five and ten years of age also had a significantly higher incidence among the delinquents ($p < 0.01$), but loss occurring after ten years of age did not. (The Gluecks' report unfortunately does not distinguish loss of mother from loss of father.)

Wardle,[123] studying cases in a child guidance clinic, investigated the association of three sets of antecedent conditions with the type of behaviour problem shown by the child: (a) homes broken by the loss of one parent through death, divorce or separation; (b) mother-child separations of more than six months in duration; and (c) one parent having come from a broken home. Conduct disorders, including stealing, occurred significantly more frequently among children from broken homes, among those in intact homes who had been separated from their mothers, and among those whose parent or parents themselves had come from broken homes. Neurotic disorders were found more frequently among children from intact homes, among children who had not suffered mother-child separation and among those whose parents had come from intact homes. No significant differences were found, however, between those children from broken homes who had been separated from their mothers and those who had not. Wardle suggested that the high incidence of conduct disorders in children whose parents had come from broken homes is a manifestation of a vicious cycle, starting with a home that may have been accidentally broken by death or illness, causing the child to have difficulty in interpersonal relations, in turn making it difficult for the child, in the future, to provide an affectionate, secure environment for his own children, who consequently may emerge with conduct disorders.

Andry and Naess were both concerned with separation experiences less severe than those studied by Wardle and the Gluecks, and found these to be no more frequent among delinquents than among non-delinquents. Andry,[3] in the erroneous belief that Bowlby had defined " maternal deprivation " as physical separation, and that Bowlby had given no consideration either to the deprivation that can occur *without* separation or to the amelioration or prevention of deprivation that can occur *with* separation, attempted to define separation in terms of " pure " separation. By excluding separations due to death, divorce or separation of the parents, and by confining himself to separations because of illness or evacuation, or because of the work of the parents, Andry therefore ruled out much of the very sort of deprivation experience which clearly contributed to Bowlby's original findings. Unlike Bowlby, Wardle and the Gluecks, moreover, Andry explored the separation history through a questionnaire, instead of availing himself of more reliable clinical history-taking methods, and despite the fact that obtaining a reliable separation history requires special care.[101] It seems unjustified, therefore, to conclude, as Andry does in this volume (see page 39), that maternal deprivation is not a significant antecedent in delinquency, or that hypotheses derived from research into maternal deprivation lack " clearly defined empirical referents " and are " not susceptible to empirical testing by a *practical* research method ".

Naess [84] compared the incidence of early mother-child separation in a group of 42 delinquents with that in a matched control group of non-delinquent siblings close in age. She chose this type of control group in order to equate the influence of other adverse features of family background—i.e., distortions or deprivations in parental care—that might be expected to influence both siblings. In choosing the delinquent group because of the availability of non-delinquent siblings as controls, she may well have ruled out some of the more severe and depriving instances of separation which might be expected adversely to affect all siblings near to each other in age. In any event, she found a higher incidence of early mother-child separation in the control group than in the delinquent group, even with respect to longer separations of over six months in duration.

As Andry has pointed out, studies such as Bowlby's or the Gluecks' show that a history of severe separation experiences is characteristic of only a proportion of a delinquent group. It is undoubtedly true, as he suggests, that deprivation or distortion in parent-child relations without actual separation may have been a factor in contributing to the delinquency of the non-separated remainder. On the other hand, it has frequently been assumed that there are different causes of delinquency —that " delinquency " is a phenotypical and not a genotypical concept. Bowlby himself stated that early maternal deprivation was foremost among the causes not of delinquency, but of delinquent (or affectionless or psychopathic) character formation. It is widely accepted that only a proportion of criminal or delinquent acts result from this kind of character formation. Naess [84] acknowledged this distinction, but rather than undertake a clinical assessment of her delinquent group to distinguish those with character disorders, she chose to use as a working assumption that if she selected her group of delinquents on the basis of their performing the same kind of delinquent acts (i.e., stealing, playing truant, violent behaviour, unruliness, running away, staying out late at night) as did Bowlby's affectionless thieves, she would thus ensure that they had the same character formation.

In summary, then, some delinquency seems attributable to a character disorder, in which a prominent feature is impaired capacity for the formation of affectional ties. Since early and severe maternal deprivation, often associated with the discontinuity of ties brought about by mother-child separation, is a significant antecedent of affectionless character formation, it is reasonable to find that deprivation is a significant antecedent in the proportion of delinquents who have this kind of character. Since not all who are affectionless become delinquent, however, there must be other antecedent conditions which singly or in combination are effective causes of the affectionless character's becoming delinquent. Andry's chief contribution seems to be the evidence with which he supports a hypothesis that insufficiencies or distortions in father-child interaction are important antecedents of delinquency, and hence may well be one of the conditions which differentiates between the affectionless character who becomes delinquent and the one who does not. In the meantime, the studies of Andry and Naess strongly suggest that simple mother-child separation experiences without severe deprivation are not a significantly frequent antecedent of delinquency.

How permanent are the effects of deprivation? Finally, retrospective case studies have little light to throw on the question of permanence *versus* reversibility of the effects of deprivation. Retrospective follow-up or longitudinal current studies are more appropriate strategies for exploring the extent to which impairment attributable to deprivation lessens when deprivation is relieved. The studies of Clarke & Clarke,[35-38] however, have been much cited as evidence that the effects of even severe intellectual impairment may be reversed to a substantial degree, and at an age at which the development of intelligence is generally believed to have ceased. These authors, however, deal only with the global measure of intelligence provided by the IQ, and offer evidence neither about personality nor about specific intellectual processes such as language or abstract function.

Questions unanswered by the retrospective case study strategy. It is common to comment critically about the findings of a retrospective case study: " But what of the people who have had similar experiences in childhood who have *not* turned up in a child guidance clinic, mental hospital, institution for defectives, or court? " This is a completely legitimate question, and the inability of retrospective case studies to answer it is the major limitation of this strategy. One may ask the question about children who had experiences similar to Bowlby's affectionless thieves or to Bender's cases of psychopathic behaviour disorders. One may also ask about the Clarkes' study: " What proportion of children from exceptionally adverse homes do *not* become feeble-minded, and why? " Or about Lewis's study: " What proportion of rejecting parents do *not* have children who show unsocialized aggression? " Or of Kellmer Pringle & Bossio's study: " What proportion of children who have lasting ties with parent-figures do *not* turn out to be notably stable despite institutional rearing? " These questions imply no criticism of these investigations, for such questions are inherent in the retrospective case study approach and cannot be answered by it.

Retrospective follow-up studies

The retrospective follow-up strategy is particularly designed to answer the question raised by the case study with respect to the proportion of people exposed in early childhood to a specific kind and degree of deprivation who end up with the " syndrome " that is hypothesized to result from the deprivation. This strategy, the reverse of the retrospective case study, requires selection of a group of subjects all of whom are known to have had a deprivation experience in the past, defined with a fair degree of precision with respect to type and severity, and examination of their present behaviour with a view to establishing the incidence of " effects " that have been hypothesized to result from this experience.

The early retrospective follow-up studies of Lowrey,[81] Goldfarb,[54-59, 62, 63] and Beres & Obers [13] offered dramatic evidence in support of the hypothesis that early, prolonged and severe deprivation of maternal care associated with institutionalization is significantly pathogenic. All of these studies, and Goldfarb's in particular, used a homogeneous and extreme sample. In Goldfarb's most important study [55] the sample was confined to children who had been admitted to a very depriving institution at a mean age of 4.5 months, where they remained for three years before being placed in foster-homes. It would be difficult to isolate another group with more homogeneous or more extreme conditions of deprivation. In the light of subsequent studies, it seems likely that the striking degree of severity and homogeneity of the outcomes noted by Goldfarb was a function of the severity and homogeneity of the antecedent conditions of deprivation. He found the " institution " group to be significantly inferior to a control group of foster-home children with respect to general intelligence, visual memory, concept formation, language function and school adjustment. Thirteen of the fifteen institutional children were markedly detached, isolated and incapable of deep or lasting ties, whereas this was true of none of the foster-home children. Only one of the institutional children seemed " normal " in adjustment, while nine were severely maladjusted; in contrast, ten of the controls were normal and only two severely disturbed. With respect to detailed personality characteristics and problem behaviour there were many significant differences in which the institution group was worse than the foster-home group; a few of these differences were: lack of capacity for sustained effort, inability to concentrate, intellectual apathy, restlessness, and promiscuous seeking for affection.

Recent follow-up studies concerned with deprivation and/or mother-child separation. Four follow-up studies will be discussed here. These studies are very dissimilar: Bowlby, Ainsworth, Boston & Rosenbluth [28] were concerned with the consequences of depriving separation experiences; Stott [121] dealt with the consequences of mother-child separation experiences without regard for the degree of concomitant deprivation; Chambers [34] studied a severely deprived and separated group, but with respect to only one function; Joyce Robertson [100] was concerned with the effects of insufficient mother-child interaction in infancy in the absence of separation.

Bowlby et al. [28] followed up a sample of sixty children, who had been admitted to a sanatorium for tuberculous patients sometime during their first four years of life, and who had stayed there for varying lengths of time before returning home to their parents. This sample represents much less homogeneity of deprivation experience than did Goldfarb's [55] sample, and one in which the deprivation itself was much less severe on the whole. It is therefore easy to understand, at least in retrospect, that the children's states at the time of follow-up were much more varied and in most instances much less disturbed than those found in Goldfarb's sample. The comparisons between the sanatorium group and the 180 controls were limited to an intelligence test and ratings by teachers. The latter turned out to be an unreliable instrument, and indeed the whole programme of assessment may be seen, in retrospect, as ill designed to detect the effects of deprivation that had been hypothesized on the basis of early case studies and confirmed by Goldfarb. Nevertheless the sanatorium group was found to be more frequently inclined to withdrawal and apathy and towards roughness and tempers, and less able to concentrate, than the controls. No intellectual retardation was found, but the sanatorium group seemed less capable of task involvement than the controls.

Bowlby et al. [28] attached more importance to the intensive study of the sanatorium group itself. Nearly two-thirds were found to be maladjusted enough to justify referral to a child guidance clinic. The patterns of difficulty in interpersonal relations ranged from marked over-dependence to clearly affectionless character formations.

Chambers [34] undertook a much neater but more limited follow-up study. A " deprived " group of 28 children was selected on the basis of having had at least three different foster-home placements in the first three years of life and was compared with a control group matched for age, intelligence and socio-economic level. Chambers compared the groups only with respect to ability to conceptualize time, following an hypothesis originally formulated by Bender,[12] and using four of

Piaget's experiments on time concepts. In three of the four experiments she found the deprived group significantly inferior to the controls.

A follow-up study carried out by Joyce Robertson [100] is of particular interest because it deals with deprivation in the absence of separation. She followed up twenty-five infants who had first been observed in a well-baby clinic in the first months of life, and who were later studied in nursery school. Clinic records indicated that the mothers of five of the children had been observed to have strikingly little interaction with their infants during the clinic visits, and the infants themselves were noted for poor muscular tonus, slow muscular development, weak responsiveness to the mother and to the wider environment, and lowered ability to communicate and express feeling. Later, in nursery school, these same features distinguished the five children from their age-peers. This study suggests that the well-baby clinic may provide a setting in which mothers who interact insufficiently with their babies may be identified and compared with normal mothers; detailed criteria are presented for both insufficient and sufficient mothering. This study suggests also that patterns of insufficient mothering may begin very early, and that the effects may both begin very early and persist despite later improvement in mother-child interaction.

In his follow-up study Stott [121] did not select his separated group from among those who had a more or less homogeneous deprivation experience, but from among 141 backward children. Of these 25 had suffered a substantial amount of separation during the first four years of life. Assessments of emotional development were provided by teachers on the Bristol Social Adjustment Guide, and comparable information about domestic behaviour was obtained through interviews with the mother or institutional staff. On this basis eight were classified as " well-adjusted ", eight as " unforthcoming ", five as " unsettled " and four as " maladjusted ". Nearly all the children seemed to be anxious for their mothers' approval, and were comparable in this respect to the large proportion of over-dependent children reported by Bowlby et al.[28]

Thus both Bowlby et al. and Stott found outcomes much more diverse in severity and in quality than Goldfarb had found and than early case studies had hypothesized. There seems little question that the diversity is due to the fact that both Bowlby's and Stott's groups were heterogeneous with respect to the variables believed to be significant in influencing the severity of a separation experience. Both studies used questionnaires rather than the more intensive clinical methods of assessment used by Goldfarb, and neither used the special tests of language function and abstract ability used by Goldfarb and Chambers. In both Bowlby's and Stott's studies the methods of assessment were too superficial to yield reliable evaluation of the adequacy of the processes of establishing and maintaining affectional ties. These considerations may in part account for the fact that neither study reported marked differences between the separated and control groups. Nevertheless, it is obvious that the consequences of separation were diverse in both groups. Although Bowlby et al. noted some affectionless or " superficial " children, these were a minority. Neither study reported any clear cases of delinquency. That both studies noted a high incidence of anxious attachment to the mother and over-dependence suggests that these may be significant consequences of separation experiences that are less severe than those observed as antecedents of the affectionless character.

It is not clear how much of Stott's failure to find a distinction between his separated and non-separated groups was due to their being all backward children. If by " backwardness " he meant that they were academically retarded rather than of low intelligence, all the children were in this sense, at least, maladjusted in the same way. He found severe early childhood illness to be a frequent antecedent of disturbance in both groups, and suggested that the disturbances in the separated group might have been due to childhood illness rather than to separation. Since there is so much other evidence that separation experiences, at least of the more severely depriving kind, can lead to adverse outcomes in the absence of illness, Stott's conclusion does not seem warranted. It may well be, however, that both early separation experiences and severe early illnesses are antecedents tending to make for subsequent academic backwardness.

The question of permanence of the effects of deprivation. Retrospective follow-up studies seem at first glance to be particularly suitable for an examination of the question of the permanence or reversibility of the effects of deprivation. Goldfarb's studies provide the major evidence that damage done by very severe early deprivation is resistant to reversal by subsequent relief from deprivation. Among children who were separated in early infancy and lived under conditions of severe institutional deprivation for three years, the impairment of intellectual functions did not reverse itself either soon after deprivation was relieved [60] or by adolescence.[55] Although an examination of the life-histories of such children [59] showed the personality disturbances to be more obviously overt and acute in childhood than later in adolescence,[55] the degree of reversal of the basic impairment was of limited degree.

Stott's [121] and Bowlby's [28] studies do not throw direct light on reversibility, but it may be inferred that, since Bowlby's sanatorium children had normal intelligence and both samples included a number of seemingly well-adjusted children, there had been substantial improvement of functioning in at least some cases. Beres & Obers's [13] follow-up of young adults who had spent periods of their early childhood in the same institution reported upon by Goldfarb is often quoted to show that even severe impairment may show more reversibility than Goldfarb's work implied, if the follow-up continues into adulthood. However, since Beres & Obers's sample was much more heterogeneous than Goldfarb's with respect to age at admission and length of stay (and Goldfarb, himself,[61] showed these variables to be important influences on the severity of outcome), it is not clear how much importance should be attached to the longer follow-up. In any event, the incidence and severity of the disturbance represented in Beres & Obers's sample suggests that any reversal of impairment that had taken place fell far short of completeness. Although further light is shed by current longitudinal studies upon the conditions that make impairment due to deprivation more or less readily reversible, Goldfarb's studies remain the chief evidence for the claim that very severe and prolonged deprivation beginning in the first year of life may leave grave, permanent effects on the personality.

The question of " multiple mothers ". Cultural anthropology apart, the only evidence of the influence of " multiple mothers " or " non-continuous mothering " upon subsequent development comes from follow-up studies. One kind of study is concerned with the pattern of mothering provided in the " home management houses " of home economics departments in some American universities, where infants are given mothering (presumed to approach sufficiency in total amount) by frequently shifting figures. Gardner, Hawkes & Burchinal [52] were concerned with one such house where infants are admitted at about five months of age and remain for approximately five months, during which time each infant is cared for by a succession of students, each having responsibility for the baby for a few days at a time. Twenty-nine children and adolescents who had had this kind of experience in infancy, and who had been adopted subsequently at a mean age of twelve months, were followed up and compared with a matched control group of school classmates. The assessment was done by means of paper-pencil tests of ability and personality. No significant differences were found between the groups, although the differences tended to favour the family-reared control group and the differences in the " personal adjustment " scores approached significance ($p < 0.07$). Although these findings are in line with evidence from current studies that adoptive placement as late as twelve months of age may reverse retardation due to earlier institutional deprivation, as measured by the IQ or DQ, there is no evidence with respect to the specific intellectual functions believed to be most vulnerable to the influence of deprivation in infancy. Moreover, the personality assessment instruments used were scarcely sensitive enough to detect qualitative differences in the nature of interpersonal attachments.

Different from the home management house system of rearing infants and children is the system of the Israeli *Kibbutz*. Here, several mother-figures supplement each other, while relations with parents and substitute parents remain continuous to a fairly high degree. Although one *Kibbutz* differs from another in its particular system, those reported by Spiro [114] and Rabin [90-92] have in common the fact that the responsibility for the rearing of the young child is shared by the parents, one or more nurses in the infants' or children's houses, and later by nursery school teachers. As Bowlby pointed out [16] (p. 43) this system implies in no way a complete abandonment of parent-child relations. The evidence to date suggests that *Kibbutzim* children make close and meaningful attachments to their parents, but that since the parents have little responsibility for training in socialization, the attitude of children towards parent-figures is considerably different from the attitudes of children reared in the conventional family units of other Western societies. Moreover, it seems clear that children reared under these conditions make much stronger identifications with their group of age-peers than do family-reared children.

Difficulties in the retrospective follow-up strategy. Retrospective follow-up studies are exceedingly time-consuming and difficult to execute well, which may explain why relatively few have been undertaken during the last ten years. The difficulties and inadequacies inherent in the retrospective follow-up strategy were discussed in detail by Ainsworth & Bowlby [2] and will be summarized here.

The first difficulty in the retrospective follow-up may lie in the choice of a deprived group. When the problem is one of attempting to tease out the relative contributions of various aspects of a deprivation experience, the choice of a deprived group presents serious problems. If a deprived group is chosen in terms of a reasonable degree of homogeneity of experience during the separation, as in the study of sanatorium children by Bowlby et al.,[28] it is impossible to sort out the various sources of disturbance that are associated with each other—in this case, breach of the child-mother tie, breach of other ties with home and family, deprivation attributable to lack of motherly care while in the institution, other deprivations associated with institutional life, and illness. Moreover, unless special steps are taken to control pre-separation and post-separation variables by selection (which is difficult), a seemingly

fairly homogeneous sample can turn out to be embarrassingly heterogeneous. In the case of the follow-up of sanatorium children, later
intensive interviews with parents yielded information of separation
experiences pre-dating admission to the sanatorium, with frequency,
age, duration and circumstances varying so greatly that it was impossible
subsequently to sort out the relative influence of these variables upon
outcome. If these simple factual variables create difficulty, how more
difficult still is it to evaluate retrospectively the extent and influence
of deprivation and distortion in the child's relations with his parents
at home, before and after the separation experience! To select a group
with heterogeneous separation experiences, as Stott [121] did, is no
solution; this merely adds to the total heterogeneity and to the difficulty
of sorting out the relative influence of different facets of disturbing
early experiences. The selection of an appropriate control group also
presents serious problems, which will not be discussed here.

Assessment of the state of the individual at the time of follow-up
presents difficulties also, except for the evaluation of cognitive processes,
for there is a serious deficiency of adequate quantitative measures of
personality function, and especially of interpersonal relations. Self-
report inventories place the onus for reliable reporting on the subject
himself, and questionnaire techniques place the onus on an informant
who is often an unskilled or biased witness, as in the case of teachers
or parents. The clinical diagnostic approach to personality assessment,
including both interview and projective techniques, remains by and large
the best basis of personality assessment now available, despite its well-
known drawbacks; but it is extremely time-consuming and hence
expensive to use.

Goldfarb [55] solved these difficulties better than any subsequent
investigator using the follow-up approach. He accomplished this by
selecting an " institution " group admitted at such an early age that the
effect of pre-separation experience was minimized, by having a ready-
made control group of " foster-home " children, both groups being
handled by the same agency, and by having through the case-workers
of this agency a longitudinal, comprehensive, clinical assessment of the
children of both groups, together with longitudinal information about
their foster-families. Because of the homogeneity of the institution
group, he was able to focus on a very small sample, and thus was able
to use both a large number of quantitative, cognitive tests and the more
time-consuming clinical and projective techniques.

It is to be hoped that those who plan further follow-up studies will
benefit from the difficulties encountered by the investigators of the last
ten years. It seems wisest to accept the limitation that a number of
variables are confounded in a homogeneous sample from any given

setting, and to rely upon contrast groups and comparison with the findings of other studies to sort out the influence of these variables. It is necessary to focus assessment upon specific functions already found or hypothesized to be affected by deprivation rather than to use only global measures. And it is essential to use careful assessment techniques rather than superficial or unreliable ones. With these precautions, the follow-up approach can be very useful in determining the effect of clusters of antecedent conditions that make for deprivation and in assessing the relative severity of each.

Population surveys

In 1954 Ainsworth & Bowlby [2] stated with respect to the population survey method:

> " Although perhaps attractive at first sight, an examination shows such a project to be fraught with great difficulties. For instance, collection of the data would present the same problems as are met with in the follow-up approach, multiplied many times because of the larger scope of the project. Furthermore, such a survey, if done carefully with thorough clinical appraisals of personality, would be an undertaking of such magnitude as to lie outside the limit of feasibility. Whether it would be worth undertaking on a more superficial basis is doubtful."

Wootton in this volume (see page 70) considers population surveys to be essential for the evaluation of the pathogenicity of mother-child separation. In the meantime she considers it an unproven hypothesis that early and prolonged or repeated mother-child separation can lead to grave and lasting effects. In support of this position she quotes two studies with inconclusive findings; both, however, can be cited equally well to support the position that the large-scale population survey is not appropriate for exploring the later effects of either deprivation or early separation.

Douglas & Blomfield [46] studied 4668 children through interviews conducted by local authority health visitors guided by a brief pre-determined questionnaire. Through these interviews it was found that half the children had been separated at some time during the first six years of life, although in only 14% had the separation lasted for four weeks or more. This latter group was matched with non-separated children from the same population pool. The measures of emotional disturbance were crude, as they would have to be with such a large sample. They were based on the answers to the questionnaire in regard to eating difficulties, thumb-sucking, nail-biting, nose-picking, night-terrors and bed-wetting. There was no significant difference between the separated and control groups, except when separations from both mother and home were considered.

As part of the same survey, Rowntree [104] dealt with children from broken families who had lost one parent before the age of four; 277 of these children were matched with children from unbroken families. Of the signs of disturbance covered in the questionnaire, only bed-wetting was found to have a higher incidence in broken than in unbroken families, and then only at the time of follow-up at four years of age, and not later, at six years of age. Since the mothers were in sole charge of over 80% of the children, and since the relatively small group separated from their mothers was not studied separately, this study has no light to throw on the effects of mother-child separation.

It seems entirely likely that the negative findings offered by these studies are attributable to the very superficial criteria of emotional health employed rather than to the absence of any true differences between the groups. It is because superficial and unreliable assessment of effects is inevitable in the large-scale population study that this strategy is inappropriate for exploring the effects of early deprivation and separation experiences. The small-scale follow-up study is a more promising strategy.

Experimental studies

Before the formulation of the hypothesis that prolonged deprivation experiences in early childhood have severe and lasting effects upon subsequent development, one isolated study was undertaken in which human infants were experimentally deprived. Dennis [44] reared two babies under conditions of " restricted practice and minimum social stimulation " through the first year of life, in order to test the hypothesis that patterns of behaviour emerge through maturation rather than through learning. Fortunately for the babies, the experimental conditions were not maximally depriving, since the experimenters came when the babies cried, spent long periods in their presence watching them, and gradually relaxed their self-imposed " indifference " as the patterns in which they were interested emerged. The babies took the initiative in social interaction with their caretakers and did not appear to be damaged by the experiment—although there was no adequate detailed comparison of their social and affectional behaviour with that of infants reared under normal conditions.

Now, however, laboratory experimentation introducing deprivation is considered possible only with infra-human species. Contrary to Wootton's opinion, though, most behavioural scientists since Darwin have considered findings from infra-human species of some possible relevance for the understanding of human behaviour, although it is generally acknowledged that inter-species differences make it impossible to extrapolate from one species to another without further careful research to check the applicability of the generalization. Among the most relevant animal research is that of Harlow,[65-67] who has studied the development of affectional patterns in infant monkeys. Two of his most relevant findings are the intensity and persistence of the infant primate's monotropic attachment to the mother or mother-surrogate. Recently * he reported that monkeys which had been separated from their mothers at birth and reared either in the absence of any mother-surrogate or with only an inanimate cloth mother-surrogate failed, at maturity, to show normal sexual behaviour. Despite this lack of sexual responsiveness, four females finally were mated; when their infants were born, however, they showed a strikingly abnormal absence of maternal behaviour. This report provides an instance of a " hidden " effect of an early deprivation experience that becomes overt only later.

Although it is not now possible experimentally to subject human infants to severe early deprivation, it is possible experimentally to relieve or ameliorate deprivation. Five such experiments will be reported. Reference will be made first to the studies of Skeels and his associates, which, though pertinent to a study of maternal deprivation, have been omitted from most reviews of the literature, perhaps because they were so scathingly criticized by McNemar.[82] In the light of subsequent developments, however, Skeels' findings seem likely to be valid.

Skeels, Updegraff, Wellman & Williams [112] attempted an experimental relief from deprivation in an orphanage by providing a group of pre-school children with nursery school experience, both morning and afternoon, while a matched control group spent equivalent time in the very depriving and unstimulating conditions of the orphanage. Both groups were retested at six-monthly intervals. The experimental group maintained its initial mean IQ of 82, while the control group gradually declined.

In another, less systematic, experiment Skeels & Dye [109] transferred a group of 13 orphanage children under two and a half years of age to an institution for the feeble-minded, where they were placed in a ward with older girls. The mean IQ improved from 64 to 92 over a mean period of 19 months, and seven of the children were then adopted and maintained at least average IQs. The IQs of a contrasting group of children who remained in the orphanage declined, by the end of the study, from a mean of 87 to one of 61. Skeels & Dye attribute the improvement of the experimental group to the establishment of an attachment to one adult, for each child had one person, older girl or attendant, who " adopted " him and performed for him the major mothering

---

* " Mother-infant interactions of monkeys ", a paper delivered at a meeting of the Tavistock Study Group on Mother-Infant Interaction, London, September 1961, the proceedings of which are to be published.

functions. The striking improvement in IQ of this group, which was given the opportunity for attachment to a mother-surrogate, contrasts with the lack of improvement of the group given nursery school experience in the orphanage ; the nursery school experience seemed helpful in arresting the decline attributable to the extreme deprivation of the orphanage, but seemed unable to reverse it.

Prugh, Staub, Sands, Kirschbaum & Lenihan [89] studied the reactions to hospitalization of children between two and twelve years of age, experimentally subjecting one group to procedures designed to minimize the traumatic impact of a hospital experience, and comparing this group with a control group cared for in the customary way. They found that the disturbance of the children both while in hospital and after returning home was less marked in the experimental than in the control group, although the experimental improvements in hospital procedure were less helpful to children under four years of age than to the older children.

Rheingold [93] gave intensive mothering to eight six-month-old institution infants, four at a time, for seven and a half hours a day, five days a week for eight weeks. During the same time a matched control group received the care typical of the institution, characterized by considerable mothering, but less in total amount than that given to the experimental group, and provided by a variety of figures. The experimental subjects became significantly more responsive socially than the controls, especially to the experimenter who mothered them. Vocalizations, especially in response to her, increased while those of the control group decreased. No significant difference was noted, however, in developmental test scores, both groups remaining throughout in the average range. The infants of both groups spent approximately nine months in the institutions and subsequently were family-reared. When re-examined at the age of twenty months,[94] no lasting differences were noted, except for a tendency among the experimental subjects still to vocalize more than the controls. Despite the fact that the experimental mothering was more intensive than the mothering ordinarily given in the institution, it doubtless was less in total weekly amount than the mothering given an infant reared in the average family, and, of course, the experimental mothering lasted for only eight weeks. In view of these considerations, it is noteworthy that differences in social responsiveness and vocalization emerged, and that the latter persisted into the second year of life.

David & Appell [41, 42] introduced an experimental régime of " intensive individualized nursing care " into a residential nursery where healthy infants of under twelve months of age lived while receiving BCG vaccination. A group of infants given intensive individualized care were compared with infants given the routine care characteristic of the nursery. The reports of this study, to date, concern a careful analysis of the differences between the individualized care and the routine care. Under routine conditions an average of 25 persons shared in the care of one child, whereas with individualized care two nurses chiefly cared for a child. The multiplicity of adults concerned in the care of a child under routine conditions by no means ensured an adequate total amount of care; on the contrary, the babies cared for in a routine way had much shorter contacts with each caretaker, and spent a much larger proportion of their waking hours in isolation than did those cared for in the experimental programme. Most striking of all were the inferior quality and quantity of the interaction between nurse and infant in the control group; the nurses were relatively unresponsive to the spontaneous behaviour of the child, and consequently there was rarely a sequence of interactions between them.

Both Rheingold's and David & Appell's studies highlight the extraordinary difficulty of arranging for individualized care of the infant in an institutional setting; even these intensive individualized programmes did not approximate to the amount of care given by a good mother to her infant at home. An examination of the details of these studies helps to explain why the so-called " maternal deprivation theorists " recommend foster-home care rather than institutional care for infants and very young children who must be parted from their mothers. Perhaps for older children a " good " institution is non-depriving, but for infants and very young children it is very difficult for any institution to be " good ". The studies by Skeels and associates suggest that it is not merely " environmental deprivation " that accounts for the depriving effects of an institution, but the absence of interaction with a mother-figure.

Current studies

Of the studies carried out during the last ten years by far the most numerous have been of children actually undergoing deprivation. Most current studies have been concerned with separation and deprivation in an institution or hospital setting, doubtless because of the obvious difficulty of obtaining access to a sample of children currently undergoing a deprivation experience while remaining with their mothers at home, but also because of the desirability of observing the child's response to the onset of the deprivation experience and his process of adjustment to it. These current studies have been concerned chiefly with the first two of the three pertinent phases of response to deprivation —the period of deprivation itself, and the period immediately after the deprivation has been relieved. Few current studies have been concerned with the third phase—the long-term period of adjustment after relief from deprivation. Some current studies have focused on the state of the child and have been essentially cross-sectional in nature, observing a given child at one or only a few points in his response to the experience; others have studied the sequence of responses, with frequent observations over a more or less extended longitudinal span.

Current studies of the state of the child during deprivation. Current studies of the state of infants and young children while subjected to depriving separations have emphasized the effect of such separations in retarding development. Roudinesco & Appell [102, 103] reported retardation in children admitted to and studied in a depriving institution between one and four years of age. The mean DQ of groups of children who had suffered different durations of separation declined progressively to 62.7 for children who had been separated for the maximum period of four months or more. This goes some way to confirm the earlier reports of Spitz [115-117, 119] and suggests that his findings were substantially valid despite the criticisms Pinneau [86] has made of his statistical methods. Roudinesco & Appell found age differences in the course of retardation, with children above the age of 2 years and 10 months being more dramatically affected at the onset of separation but resisting subsequent retardation better than the younger children, whose decline was slower but eventually more profound. A comparable study was undertaken several years later [6] after some improvements had been made in the institution, including the establishment of a nursery school; the decline of DQ with continuing separation was less, but there was still a decline. Rheingold [93, 94] is among the few observers who have not reported a progressive decline in IQ with continued institutionalization ; the mothering given in her institution seemed superior to that given in the institutions reported upon by Spitz and Roudinesco-Aubry, although it was provided by a variety of different adults. Moreover, the infants were reared in families after 12 months of age.

Even these few studies have some pertinence to the controversial question of the variables involved in institutional deprivation. It seems clear that institutions can vary in the severity of the deprivation they offer and that their variation is significantly related to the severity of the effect on the child, a point that Wootton has stressed (see page 66). That progressive intellectual retardation can occur as a result of deprivation without separation was demonstrated by an earlier study of Skeels & Fillmore [110] in which older children in seriously underprivileged homes were found to have lower IQs than younger children. In general, it would seem that, regardless of the setting in which it occurs, continuing deprivation has a progressively retarding effect.

The specific aspects most seriously affected by continuing deprivation have been found repeatedly to be language and social development, even as reflected in as global an assessment as the Gesell DQ.[6, 102, 103] Skeels and associates [112] were perhaps the first to note a specific retardation in language among deprived children. Deficiency in language and abstract function were also stressed in Goldfarb's studies of institutional children.[55, 60]   More recently, Kellmer Pringle & Bossio [87, 88] found that institution children tested on a variety of measures of language development received mean scores that were markedly retarded.

Evidence of reversibility of retardation is not to be found in the foregoing studies, which consider global measurements of development (by means of IQ or DQ) of children in a continuing condition of unrelieved deprivation. Dennis & Najarian,[45] however, submitted evidence which they interpreted to show that intellectual retardation can spontaneously reverse itself, but their inferences are open to serious criticism. They tested two groups of children in a very depriving institution in Lebanon. The children aged less than twelve months were severely retarded, with a mean Cattell IQ of 68. The children from four and a half to six years of age, who had continued in this very depriving environment since early in the first year of life, were, they claimed, only 10% below the American norms in tests of intelligence, and hence not significantly retarded. The tests they used were, however, confined to only a few performance tests. In making their selection of tests they argued that retardation in language function could be expected, implying thereby that language function is unrelated to intelligence—despite the fact that sub-tests involving language function in intelligence scales are the sub-tests most highly correlated to total IQ. Their findings with respect to performance test scores were highly comparable to those of Goldfarb [60] and Kellmer Pringle & Bossio,[88] who showed that institution children are close to normal in several performance test scores, although markedly retarded in global scores and in specific language scores. Dennis & Najarian excused themselves from reporting on the social behaviour of their deprived groups on the grounds that there are no adequate tests of personality and social function for the infant and young child. They did, however, report that the older group seemed friendly, but this, of course, could mean no more than the indiscriminate seeking for contact that has been reported as typical of the extremely deprived child since Levy,[77] Goldfarb [55] and Bender [12] first noted it. Since they excluded adequate examination of those very functions found by previous workers to be most affected by prolonged early deprivation, Dennis & Najarian were unjustified in concluding that their study demonstrated that the effects of continued severe deprivation are negligible.

Current studies of the state of the child after relief from deprivation.
The current studies of the state of the infant or young child after relief
from deprivation are pertinent chiefly to the question of how readily
reversible is the intellectual retardation attributable to deprivation.
Skeels & Harms [111] followed children with very inferior social histories
from their admission to a depriving orphanage and to subsequent adoption before the age of two years. Even those 87 children whose mothers
had IQs below 75 were found to have a mean IQ of 106 when tested
after adoptive placement. In a later study Skodak & Skeels [113] followed
100 children who had been adopted in infancy from this same orphanage,
and found that their slightly above average mental development had
been maintained into early adolescence. This relief from severe deprivation produced beneficial effects in striking contrast to the progressive
decline in IQ found for children who continued in the same orphanage.[109, 112]

Fischer [49] followed a group of low-scoring institutional infants,
of whom those who had been testable had a mean IQ of 76 at six to
seven months of age. She found that 72% had been adopted at a mean
age of eleven months, and that when re-examined at twenty months
they obtained a mean IQ of 98. Relief from deprivation through adoption in infancy thus seems to reverse general intellectual retardation,
even when adoption is as late as the end of the first year of life (or
possibly later, to judge from Skeels & Harms).

Aubry [6] and her associates gave to a few individual children (who
had suffered extreme damage from early, severe and prolonged deprivation) intensive psychotherapy, with strikingly hopeful results in some
cases. Monique's DQ, for example,[4, 5, 40] improved from 35 at two
years of age to 97 after seventeen months of therapy; only her language
remained below normal; her general behaviour improved considerably.

From this group of current studies of response to relief from deprivation (and from comparable experimental studies), it seems clear
that the progressive retardation of *general* development (as measured
by the DQ or IQ) that occurs during severe deprivation may be arrested
or reversed if relief is provided within the first two years of life, and
perhaps especially within the first twelve months. The provision of
mothering by one mother-figure seems more effective in reversing the
retardation, even in an institutional environment, than other types of
" environmental stimulation ". Striking improvement may be obtained
through intensive psychotherapy in the case of some children too
detached and unresponsive to benefit from a mother-surrogate. This
group of studies does not, however, throw much light upon the possible
reversal of impairment to those intellectual and personality processes
that are now known to be *specifically* vulnerable to disturbance through

deprivation; indeed, there is some evidence that language, for example, may remain impaired. The conclusion that the damage of early deprivation can be reversed completely by subsequent relief from deprivation is, therefore, not yet justified.

On the other hand, the studies discussed above give more grounds for optimism about at least partial reversibility of damage than did Spitz's report.[117, 119] Spitz's view was based on a group of infants who suffered severe " anaclitic depression " when separated from their mothers at some time between six and nine months of age. Although those who were reunited with their mothers after separations of less than five months (and especially after separations of less than three months) rapidly re-established their previous rate of development, those who had been separated for more than five months did not. Spitz quoted a mean decline of 25 DQ points during the separation of five months or more and a further decline of 4 points during the first eighteen months after reunion with the mother. He concluded that the retardation attributable to the " depression " is not reversible if the depriving separation lasts longer than five months. The discrepancy between this finding and the findings of the adoption studies mentioned above may be attributable to the fact that Spitz's depressed infants had suffered a severely depriving separation after having established a relationship with the mother, whereas Fischer's infants, for example, had spent most of the first year of life in an institutional environment without opportunity to establish a relationship with a mother-figure. It must be noted that Spitz's argument is based only on infants who were severely depressed following separation and not on the total group of separated infants. On the other hand, all the severely depressed infants had had good pre-separation relationships with their mothers, and may be described as having formed a strong attachment. All the infants who failed to show depression after separation both had bad (or weak) pre-separation mother-child relations and were assigned to a substitute mother while separated. These considerations suggest that a depriving experience in the first year of life may cause retardation that is less readily reversible if it is contingent upon a breach of the mother-child tie than if it is not.

Current studies of the processes of response to separation and reunion. Current studies which have focused on the sequence of responses of infants and young children to separation with concomitant deprivation and to subsequent relief from deprivation have emphasized social responses. These social responses are sufficiently clear-cut to be distinguishable, in the absence of formal measuring devices, by simple observational techniques.

The earliest of these current studies, reported by Burlingham & Freud,[32, 33] is of particular interest because it describes the responses of infants and young children to separation from the mother and their subsequent adjustment to an institutional setting in which great effort was made to avoid deprivation. It is clear from Burlingham & Freud's reports that obvious disturbance resulted from mother-child separation as early as the second half of the first year of life, and that this distress was often strikingly persistent in children of two or three years of age. Even after the obvious distress had disappeared, the underlying disturbance of mother-child relations showed itself through the child's inability to relate normally to the mother during her visits, or, at least initially, upon returning home. Another point of particular interest was the change that occurred in young children after the practice was instituted of assigning to each child one member of the staff to act as a special mother-surrogate; the children responded to this change by a sudden, spontaneous, intense and (at first) anxious attachment to the substitute mother, and by a marked increase in social responsiveness and amenability to " educational influence ". Burlingham & Freud also noted the difficulties, because of changes of staff, in maintaining the surrogate-mother system in an institution, and pointed out that changes meant further painful separation for the children.

Robertson [29, 30, 95-99] observed children undergoing separation experiences between the ages of one and four years, in more or less depriving institutional settings, and paid particular attention to the effects of the disruption of the relationship that had already been established between the child and his mother. Three phases of response to separation were observed: (a) *protest*, characterized by crying and acute distress at the loss of the mother and by efforts to recapture her through the limited means at the child's disposal; (b) *despair*, characterized by increasing hopelessness, withdrawal, and decreasing efforts to regain the mother, for whom the child seems to be mourning; (c) *detachment* (earlier termed " denial "), characterized behaviourally by " settling down " in the separation environment, accepting the care of whatever substitute figures are available, with marked loss of attachment behaviour towards the mother. Believing that these responses, together with the responses to subsequent reunion with the parents, could not be adequately accounted for by existing theoretical accounts of the development of mother-child relations, Bowlby undertook a reformulation of theory, stemming primarily from psychoanalytic theory but also influenced greatly by the work of ethologists such as Lorenz,[79, 80] Thorpe [122] and Hinde.[70-72] This theoretical formulation has been presented by Bowlby in a series of papers,[17-20, 22-27] of which there are more to come. In these papers he proposed a new view of the origins and development of the child's tie to the mother, and a reinterpretation of separation anxiety, grief and mourning, and the defences that follow loss, particularly as they occur in the young child. This new formulation has been subject to criticism by fellow psychoanalysts, some of it severe (e.g., Schur [107]), but those who have been most productive themselves in research into maternal deprivation (e.g., Anna Freud,[51] Spitz,[118] and Lebovici in this volume (see page 75) find more common ground for agreement than disagreement.

Robertson followed some of the separated children for varying lengths of time after their reunion with parents. The responses to reunion seemed to depend very largely upon the phase of response to separation that the child had reached by the end of the separation experience. Those children who had not reached the detachment phase, and especially those who were still manifesting protest, responded to their mothers after reunion with behaviour indicating separation anxiety. They clung to their mothers more than previously, followed them wherever they went, and became very anxious when parted from them, however briefly. This pattern of responses was typical of children with previously good mother-child relations and relatively brief separations. (It was observed also in a child who had been hospitalized for as long as 23 months; this child was, however, 39 months old when she entered hospital, and older than any of the other children who had prolonged separations.) Although some children after brief separation showed this anxious, clinging response immediately upon reunion, some did so only after a period of delay, during which there was first a period either of detached strangeness or of overt hostility to and rejection of the mother. When the separation had been brief, the anxiety tended to disappear after a few weeks, but it could be readily mobilized again by a new threat of separation; this vulnerability to separation anxiety seems to be one of the effects of separation that may remain hidden for long periods. If, however, the child had experienced a long separation (for six months or more) in a hospital without substitute mothering, and had become well entrenched in a detached phase, he did not cling to his parents after reunion, nor did he regain a normal degree of attachment.

A few of the children observed during separation by Robertson have been followed for twelve years since their reunion with their parents. The findings have to date been published in only a fragmentary way.[1, 125] Despite the fact that the cases are few, but rather especially because of the scarcity of long-term longitudinal studies of separated and deprived children, it is hoped that a comprehensive account of the findings will be made available. Particularly problematical is the question of the interaction between the original separation-deprivation experience and subsequent events. Robertson reports,* for example, that one child who was detached by the end of a prolonged separation returned to a home that was soon disrupted by the loss of the father. The mother, disturbed by this loss, became overtly neurotic and could not respond warmly and patiently to a difficult and unresponsive child. The child, in turn, became so disturbed that he has been placed in one institution after another. Some of the children, especially those who returned to stable homes and to parents who persisted in offering the opportunity of affectionate interaction, were able, in many respects, eventually to adjust at a fairly stable level. All these children who had suffered prolonged, early, and severely depriving separation experiences, however, seemed to share a common impairment—namely, an inability to form and maintain close and mutually satisfying interpersonal ties—although the manifestation of this impairment differed from child to child.

The responses to separation and reunion described by Robertson are, by and large, confirmed by other studies. Jessner and associates,[75, 76] observing children during brief hospitalization for tonsillectomy, noted protest behaviour, and concluded that, in children younger than five years, anxiety in this situation is related to separation from parents and admission to a strange environment rather than to the operation or narcosis. After reunion, most children reacted mildly for a few days, but some—mainly children who had had poor pre-separation relations with their mothers—suffered severe and persistent disturbance. Jackson, Winkley, Faust & Cermak [74] followed children aged three to eight years through a tonsillectomy experience and their return home. They reported that the common initial response to reunion was babyish and clinging behaviour with sleep disturbance. After three months 16% still seemed disturbed.

Prugh, Staub, Sands, Kirschbaum & Lenihan [89] studied the reactions to hospitalization of children between two and twelve years of age. Although all children showed some initial disturbance, it was most marked in the group between two and four years old, and was usually clearly related to separation from their parents. After reunion, separation anxiety and increased dependence were the most common responses, especially among the younger children (but also among some older children); and the anxiety was most devastating in children who were already neurotic.

Aubry and her associates [6, 43] observed the early reactions to separation and institutional placement of children in the second year of life, and emphasized the frequency of initial distress, although its intensity and duration were found to depend on a number of factors. They also

---

* Personal communication.

emphasized the severe disturbances of personality that may result from prolonged separation with inadequate substitute mothering.

Heinicke [69] undertook a current study of a small sample of children between the ages of 15 and 30 months newly admitted to a residential nursery, comparing them with a day-nursery group with only partial separation. Both groups protested against the separation, but the protest of the residential group was significantly greater. Both groups had opportunity to form attachments to nursery staff, and both did so as time went on, but the residential group did so more intensely and ambivalently, being more resistant to adult demands and especially showing more frequent and more intense hostility. When the children in the residential group returned home after three weeks, their responses to their mothers were predominantly negative, either detached or actively rejecting, while all of them showed a striking preference for their father (who had been able to visit during the separation), some clinging to him and protesting against any absence from him. By the end of the third week at home, the children seemed " more or less back to normal ", although Heinicke expressed some reservations.

Flint [50] devised a diagnostic check-list to assess the degree of security and mental health of babies from birth to two years of age. The items gave much more attention to response to routines and to the physical environment than did the other current studies mentioned above. Even so, Flint reported marked differences over a two-year period between infants in an institution and " well-adjusted " family-reared infants. This difference was not great during the first six months of life, but became more and more marked as the scores of the institutional infants declined through the next eighteen months. A third group of " poorly adjusted " infants had been separated from their own mothers and were living in foster-homes to which they were reported to be making a poor initial adjustment. These infants initially scored lower than the institutionalized group, but their scores tended to improve slightly as time went on, while the institutional group's declined.

Although Flint's items were graded according to the age of the infant, her report did not highlight the differences in behaviour between infants of different ages, nor did she concern herself with the response to separation as such. A study by Schaffer,[105, 106] however, helped to clarify the effect of age on the response of the infant to separation during the first year of life. Schaffer observed the responses of infants, aged from three to fifty-one weeks, admitted to a children's hospital. In observing initial responses, he excluded children whose normal responsiveness might be affected by fever, pain or other features of the illness as such. He found two major patterns of response, one characteristic of infants under seven months of age and the other of infants over seven months, with so little overlap as to suggest a saltatory rather than a gradual development. The older group displayed the protest pattern described by others as typical of children between one and four years of age. The younger group, however, did not protest; they exchanged the mother for the new caretakers, and adapted themselves to the gross change in their environment with little overt disturbance. They were, however, noted throughout for being very quiet, neither crying nor vocalizing. This confirmed the earlier reports of Burlingham & Freud [32, 33] of the relatively ready adjustment of infants in the first months of life to a residential nursery. Schaffer did not observe any instance of profound deterioration—termed " hospitalism " by Bakwin [7, 8] and Spitz [115]— but the longest period of hospitalization Schaffer studied was 49 days, and about half of his infants were visited daily by their parents. On the other hand, Schaffer's findings are in line with Spitz's insistence [117] that the response to a depriving separation of an infant in the first six months of life differs from that of an infant in the second six months.

After the infants were sent home, Schaffer received reports of their behaviour from the parents—this time including in the sample the infants who were too severely ill to be observed initially. The counterparts of the two syndromes of response to separation were noted. Infants who had been *over* seven months of age when separated showed the anxious over-dependent response described by others as characteristic of children from one to four years of age upon returning home after brief separations. In every case infants who had been *under* seven months of age when separated failed to show this syndrome, most of them manifesting what Schaffer termed a " global syndrome ", characterized by inactive quiet preoccupation with the environment, by a scanning of surroundings without particular focus, and by a lack of responsiveness to social advances. This latter syndrome was reported by parents to vary in duration from twenty minutes to four days. Schaffer attributed the emergence of this " global syndrome " to the deprivation of perceptual stimulation experienced in hospital, since the infant normally receives most of his stimulation through infant-adult interaction, relatively infrequent in hospital. He suggested that the perceptual deprivation caused the child to regress to an earlier undifferentiated state in which he tended to merge with his environment ; but following the geographical change of either his return home or of a transfer within the hospital itself, this regression reversed itself and the " global syndrome " resulted. (It may be noted that two infants under two months of age were not apparently affected by either separation or reunion.)

Fischer [49] threw some light on the response of infants to a prolonged stay in an institution, although this was one in which there was less deprivation than in Spitz's foundling home or Schaffer's hospital. Fischer was concerned chiefly with the one-third who by six to seven months of age were below average in IQ. She observed a particular deficiency in grasping behaviour, despite normal strength. The retarded infants fell into two main groups: one was passive in all areas, with social reactivity limited to opening the mouth as though expecting food; and the other was very eager for interpersonal relations, so that toys and test materials evoked no responses, but the withdrawal of adult attention evoked active efforts to recover attention. It is interesting to note that both groups of infants were at the dividing point in age which distinguished the two syndromes noted by Schaffer, although Fischer's passive group was more unresponsive than Schaffer's younger separated group, and although Fischer's active group seemed to be manifesting a readiness for attachment by actively seeking it rather than protesting against the breach of an attachment already established.

The findings of these current studies concerned with the sequence of responses to separation and reunion have considerable pertinence to some of the controversy about the effects of maternal deprivation, but the pertinence is perhaps not always immediately apparent. First, the diversity among after-effects of separation experiences is related to the phase of response to separation itself, which is in turn influenced by variables such as age at separation, length of separation, availability of substitute mothering during separation, maintenance of some contact with parents, and also the nature of pre-separation adjustment and relations. It is significant that the two major patterns of behaviour reported in follow-up studies of separated and deprived children correspond to those reported in current studies: anxious over-dependence on the one hand, and superficiality or affectionlessness on the other (follow-up studies); the anxious clinging response following reunion after relatively brief or mild separations on the one hand, and the detachment and failure to re-establish affectional relations after long and severe separations on the other (current studies).

Secondly, it is noteworthy that similar initial responses to separation and reunion were noted whether the separation involved illness or not, and whether substitute mothering was available or not, at least for the child old enough to have established an attachment to a mother or substitute mother. It seems likely that the presence of a substitute-figure during a long separation could make a profound difference to development after reunion, although this is not covered by the current study data yet available. It is clear from the present evidence, however, that the breach of a tie once established is in itself disturbing, and there is the suggestion that reunion with the parents may be disturbing even in instances where there has been fairly adequate substitute mothering during separation, perhaps in part because of the breach of the new tie with the substitute-figures.

Thirdly, it is clear that separation specifically influences the relations of the child to parent-figures, and it seems reasonable that either prolonged deprivation of interaction with a substitute mother during separation or repetitions of separation can bring about the impairment of interpersonal relations that seems to be the outstanding long-term effect of severe separation-deprivation experiences.

Fourthly, with respect to reversibility, follow-through studies of children after reunion suggest that the overt disturbances after brief and/or less severe separation tend to diminish fairly readily, except in cases where the child-mother relation was originally distorted, and provided that subsequent separation or deprivation experiences do not reinforce the processes activated by the separation in question. That the overt disturbance disappears, however, does not mean that the separation experience has had no lasting effect; on the contrary, increased sensitivity to separation anxiety is at least one " hidden " effect that is grossly observable when there is a new threat of separation. The overt disturbance after prolonged and severely depriving separations is clearly severe and prolonged; to what extent such disturbance diminishes, and to what extent permanent impairment of an overt or covert nature results, is, at present, only to be surmised from the results of retrospective studies, except for the evidence provided by Robertson's few, still unpublished, cases, in which there has been a long-term longitudinal follow-through study.

The current studies already completed and reported upon, especially those indicating through what processes deprivation experiences wreak their adverse effects, suggest the desirability of further current studies, to include a variety of different deprivation conditions. Although these studies are time-consuming, the returns are more fruitful than the equally time-consuming retrospective follow-up studies. Although the cross-sectional type of current study has yielded important data, it is the longitudinal type that seems to be most promising for filling in the gaps in our knowledge of the effects of maternal deprivation. Much of the contemporary prejudice against longitudinal studies is directed towards long-term longitudinal studies. These long-term studies are expensive to undertake, and have the major fault that the questions that are asked at the outset and the techniques used to explore these questions may be obsolete twenty or twenty-five years later. Short-term longitudinal studies, on the other hand, are undoubtedly feasible, and the light they throw on developmental processes, supplemented by the information yielded by retrospective studies with respect to long-term effects, makes them an effective strategy. Some of the controversy about the long-term effects of early childhood experiences will perhaps never be resolved to everyone's satisfaction in the absence of long-term longitudinal studies; therefore, such long-term studies of at least a few cases, selected to represent specified constellations of early experience that are believed to be pathogenic, are clearly desirable.

CONCLUSIONS AND NEW DIRECTIONS

An examination of the evidence should leave no doubt that maternal deprivation in infancy and early childhood indeed has an adverse effect on development both during the deprivation experience and for a longer or shorter time after deprivation is relieved, and that severe deprivation experiences *can* lead in some cases to grave effects that resist reversal. This conclusion is essentially the same as Bowlby's in 1951. Research both during the last ten years and previously, however, makes clear that these adverse effects differ in nature, severity and duration, and that these differences are themselves related to qualitative and quantitative differences in the deprivation experience. The nature and severity of the deprivation experience are now known to be determined by an interacting and complex set of variables, although much further research is required before the relationship between antecedent depriving conditions and their effects can be specified in detail. In the meantime, certain interim conclusions can be drawn, which, in turn, point towards new directions for research.

Diversity of early experiences subsumed under the term " maternal deprivation "

Deprivation conditions differing in kind may be equivalent in severity, and may lead to effects that appear to be similar in nature and severity. Severe maternal deprivation is now known to occur under the following diverse conditions: (*a*) when an infant or young child is separated from his mother or permanent mother-substitute and cared for in an institution where he receives insufficient maternal care; (*b*) when a young child undergoes a series of separations from his mother and/or substitute mother-figures to whom he had formed attachments; (*c*) when an infant or young child is given grossly insufficient maternal care by his own mother or permanent substitute mother and has no adequate mothering from other figures to mitigate the insufficiency of mother-child interaction. Although this much is known, more remains to be discovered about the severity of the effects that can be expected to follow from variations in severity of these three main sets of conditions and combinations thereof. With respect to deprivation experiences following separation of child from mother, in which the variables influencing the severity of the separation can be specified more or less reliably, it is believed that careful retrospective follow-up studies with small, homogeneous samples can help to identify the clusters of conditions leading to more or less severe and lasting effects, and the variables serving as mitigating conditions.

There is much evidence that the discontinuity of relations brought about through separation from the mother-figure or surrogate-figure (after an attachment has been established and before the child is old enough to maintain his attachment securely throughout a period of absence) is in itself disturbing to the child regardless of the extent to which the separation ushers in a period of deprivation or insufficiency of interpersonal interaction. In order to sort out the influence of discontinuity of mother-child relations from the influence of insufficiency of mother-child interaction—i.e., to distinguish between the effects of separation and deprivation—it will be necessary to study young children who are *not* deprived during prolonged separation from their mothers and to compare them with children who are deprived during otherwise equivalent separation experiences. Moreover, longitudinal current studies of infants and young children undergoing repeated separations from their mothers or surrogate mothers would do much to clarify the processes through which cumulative separation experiences result in effects seemingly equivalent to those of prolonged and severe early deprivation.

It is now clear that deprivation occurring without physical separation can in fact be as pathogenic as deprivation occurring with separation. It has been suggested that a distinction should be maintained between deprivation and distortion in mother-child interaction. Until proved otherwise, it must be assumed that the outcome of a prolonged period of insufficiency of interaction differs from the outcome of a prolonged period in which there is a sufficiency of interaction but of a distorted nature. Although both types of experience may lead to grave effects that resist later reversal, a study of these effects is hindered by confusion between the antecedents. It is difficult enough that often (but by no means always) insufficiency and distortion of interaction are correlated— that is, the little interaction that a deprived child may have with his mother may be distorted, say, by rejection, or a distorted infant-mother relationship may result in a separation experience which itself brings insufficiency of interaction with any mother-figure. In fact, the variables of " insufficiency ", " discontinuity ", and " distortion " are often confounded. Although a major aim of scientific investigation is to differentiate between the effects of variables, research in which combinations of insufficiency, discontinuity and distortion are used is not entirely unhelpful. On the contrary, such research should help to identify some of the most pathogenic of early childhood experiences in which two or three of these variables seem to be combined.

The scientific study of deprivation experiences occurring in the context of an unbroken relationship with the mother presents more difficulties than the study of deprivation ushered in by separation, for the variables are less easily identified and classified or quantified, and access to relevant cases is often difficult until after the child has emerged with obvious damage. Joyce Robertson's study [100] in a well-baby clinic suggests that in such a setting the selection of a sample for a longitudinal study might be accomplished either by identifying depriving mothers early or at least by identifying on the basis of the mother's history " at risk " cases likely to yield a high incidence of insufficient or distorted mother-child interaction. Otherwise the retrospective case study remains the chief exploratory strategy. In using this strategy to explore the distinction between insufficiency and distortion in the pattern of mothering, it seems good sense to follow the classic pattern of careful identification and clinical description of a syndrome, careful clinical exploration of the history to identify and specify the antecedent conditions, and flexibility in delineating the antecedents that seem to be associated with the consequent outcome.

" Multiple " versus " supplementary " mothers

Perhaps because most research into the effects of maternal deprivation has been carried on in the institutional setting where any single child is cared for by a multiplicity of caretakers, it has become commonplace to assume that the so-called " maternal deprivation theorists " claim that any deviation from an exclusive mother-child pair-relationship results in deprivation. It seems necessary here to distinguish between the following patterns: (a) the presence of a major mother-figure who may give sufficient care to the child but who is replaced at frequent intervals by another mother-surrogate, with resulting discontinuity in mother-child relations (this " serial multiplicity " occurs in " home management houses " and can also occur in a family in which the parents turn over the responsibility for child care to a shifting succession of nursemaids or housekeepers); (b) the absence of a major mother-figure, and the dispersal of responsibility for the care of the child among a large number of figures, who together give an insufficient amount of opportunity for child-adult interaction (this pattern is characteristic of many hospitals and of some residential nurseries and other children's institutions); (c) both multiple and discontinuous caretakers (this is the pattern inevitably experienced by a child who has a prolonged stay in a hospital where there is a policy of rotating staff through various services); (d) the dispersal of responsibility for the care of the child among several (not many) figures who together give sufficient care, and who have a high degree of continuity (this pattern exists in many families, even in Western societies, where there is a major mother-figure who is chiefly responsible for the child's care, but whose care is supplemented by that of other members of the household; it is also characteristic of some experimental societies such as the Israeli *Kibbutzim*).

These different patterns may have different effects on development according to the degree of insufficiency or discontinuity of maternal care which may accompany them. As David & Appell [41, 42] and others have pointed out, a multiplicity of mother-figures tends to obviate sufficient adult-child interaction. In most institutions where each child, in the course of a day, has many caretakers, each adult has partial responsibility for many children. Under these circumstances two factors combine to give insufficiency of interaction: the adult does not have time to give much stimulation to any one child; the adult cannot be sensitive to the behaviour of any one child, so that he does not respond to many of the child's potentially social signals. Rheingold [93] has demonstrated that this pattern of caretaking makes for decreased social responsiveness in the infant under twelve months of age, even in an institution where the total amount of care given to each child is not grossly and obviously insufficient. If deprivation of this kind is extreme, or prolonged into the second year of life and beyond, the result can include the grave effects which, by now, are well known.

The pattern of the " home management house " with discontinuous mother-figures (" serial multiplicity ") may be expected to lead to different results, although there has not yet been intensive enough research in this direction. If this pattern of mothering provides a sufficient amount of adult-child interaction, social responsiveness may develop but may remain indiscriminate. Under these circumstances the child, perhaps therefore delayed in forming attachments to specific figures, may, if the discontinuity persists long enough, develop an " affectionless " character, incapable of attachment. There are no data, however, about children who have experienced this pattern of mothering past ten months of age. Those children who experienced this pattern up to ten months of age, however, and who were then placed in families have not manifested damage discernible through paper-pencil tests of ability and personality. It is to be hoped that the capacity for affectional ties of such children will be more intensively explored, and, more important, that observations will be made during their first year of life of their reactions to shifts in mother-figures.

Mead's contribution to this volume (see page 45) presents a thoughtful challenge to any culture-bound belief that an exclusive child-mother pair-relationship is the only satisfactory method of rearing infants and young children; indeed, she argues that such a relationship might be hazardous for survival under certain conditions. She suggests that diffusion of care among several figures may well ensure greater continuity of care and less liability to the trauma that might well come about through the loss of the mother than the exclusive mother-child pattern.

Mead argues eloquently for greater consideration of the findings of cultural anthropologists before a pattern of Western family life be assumed healthy for a non-Western society. She concedes that the institutional practices that have grown up in the West as a way of dealing with the unwanted child should be considered as a special issue, and she implies that the West should not foist upon non-Western societies an impersonal, insufficient way of caring for the unwanted child who weighs upon the collective conscience of Western society. She points out, cogently, that a major difference between Western and primitive societies is that breast-feeding is essential for survival in the latter but not in the former—a fact that makes for inevitable differences in infant-rearing practices. Her point about the vicious cycle of the mother-child pair in which the infant fails to thrive on the mother's milk, resulting in failure of milk, anxiety on the part of the mother and further failure of the child, is paralleled by Gunther's observations [64] that the shape of the mother's nipple and breast are crucial conditions for the establishment of breast-feeding in the earliest days of life. If the breast is poorly shaped and the nipple insufficiently protractile, the infant will feed lazily at best (or may even fight at the breast because of anoxia); under such circumstances the mother becomes anxious and/or depressed; if the baby is not able to establish a satisfactory breast-feeding response during the first few days, he is not able subsequently to do so.

Several aspects of Mead's position, however, are challengeable. First, she apparently believes that Bowlby (and others concerned with the adverse effects of early maternal deprivation) sponsors an exclusive mother-child pair as the ideal. This, as already pointed out, seems to be a misunderstanding of Bowlby's position. Bowlby has argued for the desirability of a major mother-figure, not necessarily the biological mother, whose care is supplemented by other figures, including a father-figure.

Secondly, she seems to imply that in some non-Western societies successful infant- and child-rearing is commonly achieved by dispersion of maternal care among " multiple nurturing figures " with no major mother-figure. Although such a pattern may be found occasionally in any society, it is not likely to be the norm in any primitive society. In the first place, in any society where breast-feeding is the norm, it seems inconceivable that the woman who regularly feeds the child would not usually be a major mother-figure, giving more care than any other figure. Moreover, even in the Israeli *Kibbutzim*, where the amount of care given by the biological mother is before long exceeded by the care given by the *metapelet*, there seems always to be a major mother-figure, whether the mother, the *metapelet*, or her successor, the teacher-nurse in charge of the nursery school; furthermore, despite some discontinuity among other figures, the tie with the biological parents remains significant and continuous, and the tie with the age-peers is not only the most continuous of all but also perhaps the most significant.

Thirdly, regardless of the system of infant-rearing common in a given society, it seems entirely likely that the infant himself is innately monotropic—that is, he tends to attach himself primarily to one specific figure, although he may well subsequently extend his attachments to other supplementary figures. His initiative in attachment behaviour is attested to by some studies of deprivation in human infants (especially Burlingham & Freud [33]), by studies of primates (e.g., Harlow [65-67]) and by a study which Ainsworth conducted in a semi-acculturated African society.* If the human infant is innately monotropic, then a situation (whether brought about by an "experimental society" or through some individual variation in a traditional society) which impedes monotropic attachment will distort the normal course of development.

Fourthly, there seems implicit in Mead's argument that if a pattern of child-rearing in a primitive society has survived, and if it can be argued that it is an appropriate preparation for the life of an adult in this society, it is therefore a desirable mode of child-rearing. Despite the emphasis that Mead gives to biological factors in survival, her final criterion seems to be cultural appropriateness of patterns. Although this is a common conclusion of studies in cultural anthropology, it can be challenged. Can we not, as Murphy [83] suggests, differentiate between societies that facilitate and those that handicap the growth of mental health—between societies that allow for and those that frustate basic biological patterns and individual differences therein?

Regardless of these possible points of difference with Mead's position, it is certainly true that study of non-Western societies is needed—studies of both Eastern European societies (some of which have, at one time or another, experimented with new patterns of family life and infant-rearing) and the non-European societies, many of which (whether characterized as primitive or civilized, acculturated or non-acculturated) have patterns of infant-rearing different from those of Western societies. In this context, the question may not centre upon insufficiency, discon-

---

* "The development of infant-mother interaction among the Ganda", a paper delivered at a meeting of the Tavistock Study Group on Mother-Infant Interaction, London, September 1961, the proceedings of which are to be published.

tinuity or distortion of maternal care as much as upon the pattern of supplementing the care of the major mother-figure, and upon the effects of different patterns on the child's development.

Finally, there are contemporary variations in the supplementary care of infants in Western societies. To a greater or lesser extent the father shares in the care of the infant and young child, and different households vary the number and continuity of other supplementary figures: relatives, older siblings, permanent or temporary part-time or full-time servants such as maids, nursemaids, mother's helpers and baby-sitters. More and more women in Western societies seem to wish to free themselves from the role of full-time mother and housewife and to share these duties with other figures in order to undertake employment outside the home. Attention has been given to the problems of young children whose working mothers have low socio-economic status, but, until recently, little interest has been taken in the problems of children whose working mothers have a higher socio-economic status.

Stolz [120] has reviewed a considerable body of research on the effect of working mothers, but very little of it has been concerned with the effect on infants and pre-school children, and none of it with the effect of the supplementary mothering arrangements that have been made. The fact that these important points have been ignored undoubtedly contributes to the general finding that the children of working mothers and the children of non-working mothers do not differ significantly.

The practical problem is not entirely solved by pressing mothers, in order to give adequate care to their infants and pre-school children, to delay resuming their careers. As illustrated by the case histories of severely deprived children described by Coleman & Provence, [39] some mothers are themselves unable to provide sufficient maternal care (at least for these particular infants), and both infant and mother might well, therefore, thrive better with the mother working and with adequate and continuous supplementary mothering arrangements provided. That this problem is a major one is demonstrated by the report of the symposium on *Research Issues Related to the Effects of Maternal Employment on Children*, [108] in which all contributors gave emphasis to the significance of the mother's need to work and all tended to minimize the possible deleterious effects on the children.

A problem of great theoretical and practical importance for future research, therefore, is the exploration of the extent to which the major mother-figure can or should share her responsibilities with other figures, with or without continuity, in order to discover those patterns (and there are probably several) which are optimal for the child's development of identification, security and subsequent mental health. Within such a programme of research, an especially important problem is the exploration of the father's relation to the infant and young child, and the effects on subsequent development of different amounts and kinds of paternal care.

Specific processes affected by deprivation

Maternal deprivation has a differential effect on different processes; most vulnerable seem to be certain intellectual processes, especially language and abstraction, and certain aspects of personality, most especially the ability to establish and maintain deep and meaningful interpersonal relations, but also the ability to control impulse in the interest of long-range goals. There is some reason to believe that the age of the child—more accurately, the state of development of the child—has an influence upon the processes affected; thus, for example, it seems reasonable to conclude from present evidence that deprivation during the first year of life affects language and abstract functioning (and indirectly the IQ or DQ) more than does deprivation later on. It seems likely that discontinuity of relations has its chief effect on the capacity for affectional ties, especially in instances where separation from mother-figures is repeated.

There are important points here for future research. First, research which purports to assess the effects of separation or deprivation experiences cannot afford to neglect assessment of these special processes known to be most vulnerable to damage. Only by establishing minimal impairment of these processes can it be demonstrated that any cluster of conditions is minimally depriving. Secondly, longitudinal research into the development of these processes seems highly desirable; only when it is known how it is that mother-child interaction facilitates development of these processes can it be understood fully how it is that insufficient interaction hinders development. Furthermore, attention needs to be given to the ways in which discontinuity of relationships affects the development of attachments.

The diverse effects of " maternal deprivation "

Diverse effects have been found to follow early childhood experiences subsumed under the term " maternal deprivation ". Some of this diversity is attributable to the fact that insufficiency, discontinuity and distortion of interactions have all been loosely classed as depriving. Even when the term " deprivation " is narrowed to cover only insufficiency of interpersonal interaction, there is still, however, diversity of effects. Both the nature and the degree of the consequent disturbance seem to be related to the degree of severity of the antecedent deprivation experience itself. Some of the diversity may be accounted for by the fact that, although the same process or processes are affected by deprivations of varying severity, the overt manifestation of the effects may be diverse. Of the variables that influence the severity of a deprivation experience, one of the most important seems to be the child's age at the onset of deprivation, for this variable seems even to determine which processes are affected. Since deprived children share with non-deprived children a great diversity of experiences, apart from and including interpersonal ones—and, to be sure, come into the world with different genetic structures—all of which make for diverse personality patterns, diversity cannot always be explained by the variables that influence the nature and severity of the deprivation experience itself. Finally, seemingly diverse effects may be due to different investigators having observed different processes with varying methods of appraisal, some of which may have been more sensitive than others.

Despite all these sources of diversity the patterns of effects seem roughly but meaningfully related to the patterns of antecedent variables, and these interrelationships deserve further intensive exploration. In this task current longitudinal studies are the most promising strategy for studying not only how the variables operative before and during the deprivation experience contribute to the responses to deprivation, but also how later experiences after deprivation has been relieved serve to reinforce, modify or reverse the processes set up during deprivation.

Some are damaged; some escape damage

That some children may emerge from a deprivation experience with grave and permanent adverse effects and others may seem to escape any severe or lasting damage is, in part, covered by the above discussion of the diversity of effects of deprivation; it is assumed that some of the puzzling differences in vulnerability to deprivation experiences will be explained by future research. If, however, future research cannot wholly account for the fact that some children are more gravely affected than others, this will constitute no valid reason for discarding the hypothesis that early deprivation experiences are pathogenic. Inexplicable differential vulnerability has been found in nearly all etiological research; it exists in instances where the chief pathogenic agent has been identified beyond any doubt and even where many of the supplementary factors making for vulnerability or resistance to the agent are known. The fact that some are exposed to the pathogenic agent and escape apparently unscathed does not constitute a valid basis for arguing against preventive efforts.

Are the effects of deprivation reversible or irreversible ?

Related to the question of differential vulnerability to a deprivation experience is the question of differential recovery from its effects. The question " Are the effects of maternal deprivation reversible or irreversible ? " surely must be restated. *How readily reversible ?* Spontaneously, without relief from deprivation, as Dennis & Najarian [45] believe possible ? Or after the ordinary relief from deprivation provided by removal from the depriving situation—through reunion with parents, or placement in an adoptive or foster-home ? Or after very careful placement to meet the particular needs of the particular child, as attempted by the reception centre of which Lewis [78] writes ? Or with once-a-week psychotherapy ? Or with intensive psychotherapy such as that reported by David & Appell ? [5, 40] *How completely reversible ?* Obviously an improvement of IQ from a defective level of, say, 55 to one of 75 implies some reversibility, but it is presumably not complete. *With respect to what functions ?* A single measure of intellectual functioning, such as the IQ, may be normal, but the individual may show impairment in specific intellectual processes such as language and abstraction. The individual may perform competently in earning a living and in ordinary social interaction with friends and colleagues and still betray impairment through failure in meeting the more intimate interpersonal demands of marriage or parenthood. *Are there hidden impairments ?* The findings both that children who have apparently recovered from a separation experience are particularly vulnerable to subsequent threats of separation, and that there is an empirical association between childhood bereavement and adult depressive illness suggest that early experiences may set up processes which may remain covert for a long time but, when subsequently reactivated by some stressful experience (which might well be minor and relatively undisturbing to other people), cause a pathological reaction. When the question of reversibility is rephrased, therefore—" How readily and completely reversible, both overtly and covertly, are the effects of deprivation and with respect to what specific processes ? "—the evidence is considerable.

The question of reversibility itself raises some further important theoretical questions about the nature of development. Three major theoretical positions seem possible.

(1) Learning theory implies that development is entirely or almost entirely a matter of environmental stimulation. When the appropriate environmental conditions are provided, learning will take place, and what has not been learned earlier can be learned later after the appropriate conditions have been introduced. According to this position, the child, initially retarded because of a deprivation in environmental

stimulation, can eventually catch up, provided that deprivation is relieved and enough time is allowed for the learning to take place. This seems to be the position taken by Clarke & Clarke [36-38].

(2) The psychoanalytic position implies that an early experience can set up certain dynamic processes that become entrenched or ingrained, and that tend to continue despite the subsequent alteration of the reality situation. Thus early maternal deprivation can be viewed as requiring the establishment of defensive operations, which serve to insulate the child against the painful frustration of seeking an interaction with an environment that is unstimulating and unresponsive. Once entrenched, this defensive operation tends to maintain itself, insulating the child against interaction with an environment that could prove supportive, responsive and helpful if he could only be receptive. According to this position, reversibility depends upon the effect of efforts to break down the defensive processes. Some of Bowlby's publications imply this position.

The defensive processes described by the psychoanalyst seem similar to certain phenomena observed in the psychology of learning; certain sequences of behaviour once well learned may be very resistant to change, and may constitute a serious block to learning a new sequence of behaviour. This interference by old habits with the learning of new habits is poignantly familiar to the golfer who first learned to slice his drive and now cannot learn to hit it straight.

(3) The " sensitive phase " or " critical period " position in psychology has been influenced by ethology, but has also emerged independently as in Hebb's [68] emphasis on early learning as an essential basis for later learning and in the work of some psychoanalysts such as Erikson. [48] This position suggests that there may be phases in the course of development during which certain processes develop normally if adequate environmental conditions are present, but if not present, development of a particular process may be arrested and subsequent stimulation may not or may only with great difficulty activate the development. This position has been given recent emphasis by Bowlby's proposal [19, 20, 23] that the development of the human infant be viewed in an ethological frame of reference.

These three positions are not mutually incompatible. It seems entirely likely that some impairment can be overcome through learning after deprivation has been relieved, while some impairment resists reversal to a greater or lesser degree because of more or less deep-seated defensive operations or habit-patterns, while still other impairment may persist because the sensitive phase of the normal development of the processes in question has been passed. (Indeed, as currently formulated, the

" sensitive phase " hypothesis is not essentially different from the psychoanalytic or " interfering-habit " position, for it is now believed that the difficulty in instituting responses not acquired in the sensitive phase is due to the emergence of other responses which interfere with them.)

The findings will be summarized in the light of this discussion:

(1) Recovery from a single, brief, depriving separation experience seems fairly prompt and complete with respect to overt behaviour under ordinary conditions; there is evidence, however, of vulnerability to future threats of separation—i.e., there is at least one " hidden " impairment that prevents the reversibility from being described as complete.

(2) Relief from deprivation after even fairly prolonged deprivation experiences in early infancy can result in rapid and dramatic improvement in overt behaviour and in generalized intellectual functioning; vocalization, however, may be retarded, even though the relief occurs before twelve months of age, and effects on other specific aspects of intellectual and personality functioning cannot be ruled out until these aspects have been explored in research.

(3) Prolonged and severe deprivation beginning early in the first year of life and continuing for as long as three years usually leads to severely adverse effects on both intellectual and personality functioning that do resist reversal.

(4) Prolonged and severe deprivation beginning in the second year of life leads to some grave effects on personality that do resist reversal, although the effects on general intelligence seem to be fairly completely reversible; specific impairment of intellectual functions has not yet been studied.

(5) The effects of age at the onset and relief of the deprivation experience are undoubtedly important factors in influencing reversibility, but these are not understood in enough detail to set precise limits for a " sensitive phase " of development of special processes.

(6) In general, in the first year of life, the younger the infant when deprivation is relieved (and hence the less prolonged the deprivation experience), the more normal is the subsequent development; yet after the first year of life has passed, the older the child at the onset of deprivation the more readily and completely reversible seem to be the effects of a deprivation of a given duration.

(7) Certain impairments seem to be less readily and less completely reversible than others—impairments in language, in abstraction and in the capacity for strong and lasting interpersonal attachments.

(8) Especially if undertaken when the child is still very young, intensive therapeutic efforts may result in marked improvement of some very severe effects that resist reversal through ordinary relief from deprivation.

(9) Subsequent experiences of insufficiency, distortion or discontinuity in interpersonal interaction may be important in reinforcing impairments that otherwise might have been reversed more or less completely.

Prompt and dramatic reversals may be interpreted in the light of relief from distress or grief or to the sudden giving way of defensive operations that had not been well entrenched. More gradual steady improvements are probably attributable for the most part to catching up through learning. A prolonged resistance to improvement may be attributable either to deep-seated defensive processes or habit patterns that interfere with the acquisition of new responses, or to the difficulty in activating development that ought to have taken place in an earlier sensitive phase. To date, the empirical evidence for the existence of a sensitive phase is clearest for language, abstraction and other symbolic functions. The sensitive phase seems to be the first year of life, most probably the second half of the first year, with the absolute upper limit of the sensitive phase still uncertain; unfortunately space does not permit a review of the evidence for this particular hypothesis.

The generalizations presented above leave many gaps to be filled through future research. In particular, more needs to be known about the normal course of development of those processes most specifically vulnerable to deprivation; indeed it is deplorable to consider how little is known about the normal course of development, in the early years, of interpersonal attachment and of those processes which later blossom into language and other symbolic processes. During the last twenty-five years child development research has focused on the child of nursery-school age and older; recently the neonate has been studied intensively. The very period which seems the most vulnerable to deprivation—the first three years of life—is largely unexplored, especially with respect to social development. Since the normal course of development is in any detail unknown, the difficulty in being precise about the effects of deprivation experiences in arresting, retarding or distorting that development is not surprising.

Even at the level of development represented by the older child and the adult, the methods of personality appraisal now available are relatively clumsy and imprecise. Conceptualization of the processes and variables to be explored is still blurred, and perhaps will remain so until there is a better understanding of the underlying developmental processes. Quantitative appraisal of personality processes seems likely to be premature, until there is clear conceptualization of the relevant variables to be quantified. For these reasons, judgements about the reversibility of impairments attributable to early interference with development by deprivation, separation or distortion in parent-child interaction seem to be very much dependent upon the level of assessment. The more superficial the assessment—and premature quantification makes for superficiality—the more evidence there is of reversibility; the more intensive, clinical and descriptive the assessment the more evidence there is of lasting damage.

None of these considerations encourages a sanguine view of the reversibility of impairment attributable to severe, early maternal deprivation experiences. Even though the effects of deprivation may be reversible somewhat more readily, more completely and more frequently than was believed possible in 1951, there are distinct limits to the readiness and extent of improvement in cases of severe impairment of long standing. Moreover, the evidence of covert and subtle effects of even a relatively mild separation experience raises doubt about the completeness of the reversibility possible in cases where early deprivation has been severe. Perhaps " complete reversibility " is an illusory product of crude methods of appraisal.

More research is obviously needed further to delimit the conditions that facilitate reversibility and to identify the types of experience in which deprivation, if unavoidable, can be minimally harmful. Meanwhile the costs of attempting to reverse the effects of early deprivation are of great magnitude—so great that every effort should be bent towards prevention.

Delinquency and deprivation

The relationship between early separation and/or deprivation experiences and delinquency remains problematical. On the one hand, retrospective case studies of psychiatrically disturbed children and adults demonstrate a significant association between character disorders, behaviour disorders and the " affectionless " character and severe, early and depriving separation experiences. Furthermore, retrospective case studies of delinquents repeatedly show a significant incidence of severely depriving early separation experiences in a proportion of the delinquent population. On the other hand, retrospective follow-up studies of children who have suffered early, prolonged and severely depriving separation experiences show a very small incidence of delinquent outcomes. Lewis's findings [78] link delinquency with parental neglect, and not with separation as such. Andry,[3] ruling out the more severe and depriving instances of maternal deprivation, found delinquency more linked to insufficiencies and distortions in father-child interaction than to maternal deprivation. Clearly, further research is needed.

If there is to be fruitful research into the validity of the proposition that some delinquent and criminal acts are the product of a special kind of character formation, which in turn is hypothesized to result from some definable kinds or combinations of kinds of experience in early childhood, certain steps seem necessary. First, to deal not with miscellaneous delinquents but with delinquents who have been assessed thoroughly enough to be classified according to their character formation is essential. Secondly, it seems unlikely that either separation or deprivation alone is the effective antecedent of delinquency, even in the " affectionless " character, but rather that the antecedent is likely to be some special form of distortion in early parent-child relations, perhaps alone, but more probably in conjunction with separation or deprivation experiences or both. Therefore, the need is for an especially thorough investigation of antecedents, with a flexible consideration of antecedent experiences in which distortion, insufficiency and discontinuity in parent-child relations are confounded. Furthermore, it seems essential to consider father-child relations as well as mother-child relations. For this type of exploration the most appropriate strategy is probably still the retrospective case study.

" Environmental " deprivation

Although it has been argued that the young child suffers from institutionalization because of " environmental " or " perceptual " deprivation, rather than because of " maternal " deprivation, this seems a tenable view only for the young infant before he is ready to form a significant attachment to a mother-figure. There is ample evidence to suggest that, for children over six months of age, throughout the second and third years of life at least, the most significant aspect of deprivation in the ordinary institution is the lack of opportunity to form an attachment to a mother-figure, either for the first time or as a substitute for an attachment that has been broken through separation. Even in the case of the infant of under six months of age, however, it seems obvious that the chief perceptual stimulation comes through the mother—in the course of caring for, handling, playing with and talking to the child. Therefore, " perceptual deprivation " seems equivalent to insufficiency of maternal care. In the case of the child over two, efforts to enrich the institutional environment by providing nursery-school experience seem to be less effective in stemming retardation of development than efforts to facilitate the attachment of the child to a substitute mother. In short, the deprivation offered by the institution chiefly stems from insufficiency of intimate interpersonal interaction.

Yarrow, in a recent, comprehensive review of the literature on maternal deprivation, [128] stresses many of the same points that have been made here—the desirability of identifying the basic variables and concepts that have been indiscriminately combined under the term " maternal deprivation ", the importance of the developmental stage at which deprivation occurs, the significance of the duration of the deprivation, and the like. Perhaps his chief emphasis, however, is upon the desirability of research to analyse the deprivation experience into its components of " sensory deprivation ", " social deprivation " and " emotional deprivation ". Even though studies such as those by David & Appell [41, 42] strongly suggest that " social deprivation " is the most significant aspect of depriving routine institutional care, further exploration is clearly desirable to ascertain the detailed nature of these components of deprivation, their relative significance, and their relation both to the variables of age at onset and duration of deprivation and to the specific processes most vulnerable to deprivation. For this task no strategy is as effective as the current study.

Other points of controversy

It now seems impossible to attribute to hereditary constitution effects that are clearly attributable to deprivation. Although undoubtedly some children may be both ill-endowed and deprived, the dramatic improvement of severely damaged children following psychotherapy, as well as the slower but still impressive improvements in intellectual level noted by Clarke & Clarke, is a clear demonstration that some apparent feeble-mindedness is of psychogenic rather than genetic origin. Similar evidence is provided by the dramatic relief from " hospitalism " shown by infants after reunion with their mothers.[7, 8] Although organic brain damage is, at least in minimal or " sub-clinical " form, now known to be much more frequent than previously believed, the same arguments apply: dramatic improvements following relief from deprivation in some cases make it impossible to assume that all infants suffering from " hospitalism " are brain-damaged—although some of them may well be. It is true, however, that the differential diagnosis between constitutional defect, organic brain damage, infantile schizophrenia and retardation attributable to severe deprivation is a difficult one to make in some cases. [6] As for the possibility that malnutrition may be responsible for the retardation of institutionalized children, diet may be a contributing factor in some institutions, but in most of the depriving institutions studied, the children did receive an adequate diet and adequate care of their other physical needs. Yet severe retardation did take place.

* * *

Although the empirical findings that have emerged from research into the effects of maternal deprivation contain no real inconsistencies when they are viewed in the light of the research strategies used to obtain them and in the light of the complex network of variables that seem to influence the severity of deprivation, it is also clear that there is much yet to be learned. Research into maternal deprivation has captured the interest and aroused the emotions of many because of the practical significance of the findings for child care. It has interested others because of the great significance of the findings for an understanding of child development. Research into maternal deprivation is chiefly concerned with a period of life that has been seriously neglected during the last three decades of research in child development. Deprivation research demonstrates the serious impact on the infant and young child of the absence of a mother, even though the child's basic physical needs may be adequately met; this immediately raises the question of the role played by the mother in normal child development. The answer to the question obviously lies in the interaction that takes place between mother and child, for if the mere physical presence of the mother were enough, the effects of deprivation would not be noticeable in the absence of separation. What interactions normally take place between a child and his mother in the period between the neonatal phase and nursery-school age—a period during which the study of interpersonal relations has been sadly neglected? Since early mother-child interaction is a necessary condition for healthy development, and particularly for social development, how does the interaction produce its effects?

Thus, although further research into the theoretical and practical aspects of maternal deprivation is desirable in order to fill in the many gaps in our knowledge, further research into the mother-child interaction that takes place in the absence of deprivation seems even more desirable. In the study of such interaction, to focus wholly on the mother, either in her need-fulfilling role or in her stimulus-providing role, is to do only half the job. The very term " interaction " implies that there is more to the infant than a bundle of needs and responses that passively waits for external stimulation to activate the responses and to fulfil the needs. The concept of the passive, recipient infant who is infinitely malleable by environmental stimulation has influenced psychological thinking and research perhaps ever since John Locke described the initial state of the human mind as a *tabula rasa*. This concept is not adequate when research turns to mother-infant interaction and its influence on development. Several questions immediately arise. What is the infant's contribution to this interaction? What behaviours that play a part in initial interaction are built into the human organism from the very first? How does the mother's response to these behaviours serve to facilitate development? What is the social function of the behaviours that emerge in the course of motor development and cognitive development (about which more is known than about social development)? In short, how does the inherent structure of the human organism interact with the structure of its environment, and especially its social environment, to shape the course of development?

The significant contribution of ethology to psychology in the attack on the above questions is that its concepts and methods have been developed to deal with precisely these questions in regard to the behaviour of infra-human species. One of Bowlby's most significant contributions during the past ten years has been to grasp the relevance of ethological concepts and methods for the study of human social development, to reformulate psychoanalytic theory with respect to the young child in the light of these concepts, and thus to provide a testable theoretical framework, which has the great present advantage of providing a feasible starting-point for the launching of research into mother-infant interaction and its influence on human development.

ACKNOWLEDGEMENT

Appreciation is due to Florence Howe of Goucher College for her invaluable editorial assistance, without which this complex review would have been considerably less comprehensible to the reader.

REFERENCES

1. Ainsworth, M. D. & Boston, M. (1952) Psychodiagnostic assessments of a child after prolonged separation in early childhood. *Brit. J. med. Psychol.*, **25**, 170

2. Ainsworth, M. D. & Bowlby, J. (1954) Research strategy in the study of mother-child separation. *Courrier*, **4**, No. 3, 2

3. Andry, R. G. (1960) *Delinquency and parental pathology*, London, Methuen

4. Appell, G. & Aubry, J. (1951) *Maternal deprivation in young children* (Film: 16 mm; 22 min; sound. Distributors: New York University Film Library; Tavistock Child Development Research Unit, London; United Nations, Geneva)

5. Appell, G. & David, M. (1961) *Case notes on Monique.* In: Foss, B. M., ed., *Determinants of infant behaviour*, London, Methuen

6. Aubry, J. (1955) *La carence de soins maternels*, Paris, Centre international de l'Enfance

7. Bakwin, H. (1942) Loneliness in infants. *Amer. J. Dis. Child.*, **63**, 30

8. Bakwin, H. (1949) Emotional deprivation in infants. *J. Pediat.*, **35**, 512

9. Barry, H. (1949) Significance of maternal bereavement before age of eight in psychiatric patients. *Arch. Neurol. Psychiat. (Chicago)*, **62**, 630

10. Barry, H. & Lindemann, E. (1960) Critical ages for maternal bereavement in psychoneuroses. *Psychosom. Med.*, **22**, 166

11. Bender, L. (1947) *Psychopathic behavior disorders in children*. In: Lindner, R. M. & Seliger, R. V., ed., *Handbook of correctional psychology*, New York, Philosophical Library, p. 360

12. Bender, L. & Yarnell, H. (1941) An observation nursery. *Amer. J. Psychiat.*, **97**, 1158

13. Beres, D. & Obers, S. J. (1950) *The effects of extreme deprivation in infancy on psychic structure in adolescence: a study in ego development*. In: *Psychoanalytic study of the child*, New York, International Universities Press, Vol. 5, p. 212

14. Bowlby, J. (1940) The influence of early environment in the development of neurosis and neurotic character. *Int. J. Psycho-Anal.*, **21**, 154

15. Bowlby, J. (1946) *Fourty-four juvenile thieves, their characters and home life*, London, Baillière, Tyndall & Cox

16. Bowlby, J. (1952) *Maternal care and mental health*, 2nd ed., Geneva (*World Health Organization: Monograph Series*, No. 2)

17. Bowlby, J. (1953) Some pathological processes set in train by early mother-child separation. *J. ment. Sci.*, **99**, 265

18. Bowlby, J. (1954) *Psychopathological processes set in train by early mother-child separation*. In: Senn, M. J., ed., *Infancy and childhood*, New York, Josiah Macy Jr. Foundation, p. 38

19. Bowlby, J. (1957) An ethological approach to research in child development. *Brit. J. med. Psychol.*, **30**, 230

20. Bowlby, J. (1958) The nature of the child's tie to his mother. *Int. J. Psycho-Anal.*, **39**, 350

21. Bowlby, J. (1958) *Can I leave my baby?* London, National Association for Mental Health

22. Bowlby, J. (1960) Separation anxiety. *Int. J. Psycho-Anal.*, **41**, 89

23. Bowlby, J. (1960) Symposium on " psycho-analysis and ethology " II. Ethology and the development of object relations. *Int. J. Psycho-Anal.*, **41**, 313

24. Bowlby, J. (1960) *Grief and mourning in infancy and early childhood*. In: *Psychoanalytic study of the child*, New York, International Universities Press, Vol. 15, p. 9

25. Bowlby, J. (1960) Separation anxiety: a critical review of the literature. *J. Child Psychol. Psychiat.*, **1**, 251

26. Bowlby, J. (1961) Processes of mourning. *Int. J. Psycho-Anal.*, **42**, 317

27. Bowlby, J. (1961) Childhood mourning and its implications for psychiatry. *Amer. J. Psychiat.*, **118**, 481

28. Bowlby, J., Ainsworth, M., Boston, M. & Rosenbluth, D. (1956) The effects of mother-child separation : a follow-up study. *Brit. J. med. Psychol.*, **29**, 211

29. Bowlby, J. & Robertson, J. (1955) *A two-year-old goes to hospital*. In: Soddy, K., ed., *Mental health and infant development*, London, Routledge & Kegan Paul, Vol. 1, p. 123

30. Bowlby, J., Robertson, J. & Rosenbluth, D. (1952) *A two-year-old goes to hospital.* In: *Psychoanalytic study of the child,* New York, International Universities Press, Vol. 7, p. 82

31. Brown, F. (1961) Depression and childhood bereavement. *J. ment. Sci.,* **107,** 754

32. Burlingham, D. & Freud, A. (1942) *Young children in wartime,* London, Allen & Unwin

33. Burlingham, D. & Freud, A. (1944) *Infants without families,* London, Allen & Unwin

34. Chambers, J. (1961) Maternal deprivation and the concept of time in children. *Amer. J. Orthopsychiat.,* **31,** 406

35. Clarke, A. D. B. & Clarke, A. M. (1957) Cognitive changes in the feebleminded. *Brit. J. Psychol.,* **45,** 173

36. Clarke, A. D. B. & Clarke, A. M. (1959) Recovery from the effects of deprivation. *Acta psychol.,* **16,** 137

37. Clarke, A. D. B. & Clarke, A. M. (1960) Some recent advances in the study of early deprivation. *J. Child Psychol. Psychiat.,* **1,** 26

38. Clarke, A. D. B., Clarke, A. M. & Reiman, S. (1958) Cognitive and social changes in the feebleminded: three further studies. *Brit. J. Psychol.,* **49,** 144

39. Coleman, R. W. & Provence, S. (1957) Environmental retardation (hospitalism) in infants living in families. *Pediatrics,* **19,** 285

40. David, M. & Appell, G. (1951) Observation et traitement d'un cas d'arriération psychogène. *J. Psychiat. infant.,* **1,** 205

41. David, M. & Appell, G. (1961) *A study of nursing care and nurse-infant interaction.* In: Foss, B. M., ed., *Determinants of infant behaviour,* London, Methuen, p. 121

42. David, M. & Appell, G. (1962) Etude des facteurs de carence affective dans une pouponnière. *Psychiat. Enfant,* **4,** Fasc. 2 (in press)

43. David, M., Nicholas, H. & Roudinesco, J. (1952) Responses of young children to separation from their mothers. *Courrier,* **2,** No. 1, 66

44. Dennis, W. (1941) Infant development under conditions of restricted practice and minimum social stimulation. *Genet. Psychol. Monogr.,* **23,** 143

45. Dennis, W. & Najarian, P. (1957) Infant development under environmental handicap. *Psychol. Monogr.,* **71,** No. 436

46. Douglas, J. W. B. & Blomfield, J. M. (1958) *Children under five,* London, Allen & Unwin

47. Earle, A. M. & Earle, B. V. (1961) Early maternal deprivation and later psychiatric illness. *Amer. J. Orthopsychiat.,* **31,** 181

48. Erikson, E. H. (1959) Identity and the life cycle. *Psychol. Issues,* **1,** 1

49. Fischer, L. L. (1952) Hospitalism in six-month-old infants. *Amer. J. Orthopsychiat.,* **22,** 522

50. Flint, B. M. (1959) *The security of infants,* Toronto, University of Toronto Press

51. Freud, A. (1960) *Discussion of Dr. John Bowlby's paper.* In: *Psychoanalytic study of the child,* New York, International Universities Press, Vol. 15, p. 95

52. Gardner, D. B., Hawkes, G. R. & Burchinal, L. G. (1961) Noncontinuous mothering in infancy and development in later childhood. *Child Develpm.*, **32**, 225

53. Glueck, S. & Glueck, E. T. (1950) *Unraveling juvenile delinquency*, Boston, Mass., Harvard University Press

54. Goldfarb, W. (1943) Infant rearing and problem behavior. *Amer. J. Orthopsychiat.*, **13**, 249

55. Goldfarb, W. (1943) Effects of early institutional care on adolescent personality. *J. exp. Educ.*, **12**, 106

56. Goldfarb, W. (1943) The effects of early institutional care on adolescent personality (graphic Rorschach data). *Child Develpm.*, **14**, 213

57. Goldfarb, W. (1944) Infant rearing as a factor in foster home replacement. *Amer. J. Orthopsychiat.*, **14**, 162

58. Goldfarb, W. (1944) Effects of early institutional care on adolescent personality: Rorschach data. *Amer. J. Orthopsychiat.*, **14**, 441

59. Goldfarb, W. (1945) Psychological privation in infancy and subsequent adjustment. *Amer. J. Orthopsychiat.*, **15**, 247

60. Goldfarb, W. (1945) Effects of psychological deprivation in infancy and subsequent stimulation. *Amer. J. Psychiat.*, **102**, 18

61. Goldfarb, W. (1947) Variations in adolescent adjustment of institutionally-reared children. *Amer. J. Orthopsychiat.*, **17**, 449

62. Goldfarb, W. (1949) Rorschach test differences between family-reared, institution-reared and schizophrenic children. *Amer. J. Orthopsychiat.*, **19**, 624

63. Goldfarb, W. (1955) *Emotional and intellectual consequences of psychologic deprivation in infancy: a re-evaluation*. In: Hoch, P. & Zubin, J., ed., *Psychopathology of childhood*, New York, Grune & Stratton, p. 192

64. Gunther, M. (1955) Instinct and the nursing couple. *Lancet*, **1**, 575

65. Harlow, H. F. (1958) The nature of love. *Amer. Psychologist*, **13**, 673

66. Harlow, H. F. (1960) Primary affectional patterns in primates. *Amer J. Orthopsychiat.*, **30**, 676

67. Harlow, H. F. (1961) *The development of affectional patterns in infant monkeys*. In: Foss, B. M., ed., *Determinants of infant behaviour*, London, Methuen, p. 75

68. Hebb, D. O. (1949) *The organization of behavior*, New York, Wiley

69. Heinicke, C. M. (1956) Some effects of separating two-year-old children from their parents: a comparative study. *Hum. Relat.*, **9**, 105

70. Hinde, R. A. (1954) Factors governing the changes in strength of a partially inborn response. *Proc. roy. Soc. B*, **142**, 306

71. Hinde, R. A. (1954) Changes in responsiveness to a constant stimulus. *Brit. J. Anim. Behav.*, **2**, 41

72. Hinde, R. A. (1959) *Some recent trends in ethology*. In: Koch, S., ed., *Psychology: the study of a science*, New York, McGraw Hill, Vol. 2, p. 562

73. Howells, J. G. & Layng, J. (1955) Separation experiences and mental health. *Lancet*, **2**, 285

74. Jackson, K., Winkley, R., Faust, O. A. & Cermak, E. G. (1952) Problems of emotional trauma in hospital treatment of children. *J. Amer. med. Ass.*, **149**, 1536

75. Jessner, L., Blom, G. E. & Waldfogel, S. (1952) *Emotional implications of tonsillectomy and adenoidectomy on children*. In: *Psychoanalytic study of the child*, New York, International Universities Press, Vol. 7, p. 126

76. Jessner, L. & Kaplan, S. (1949) *Observations on the emotional reactions of children to tonsillectomy and adenoidectomy*. In: Senn, M. J., ed., *Problems of infancy and childhood. Transactions of the Third Conference*, New York, Josiah Macy Jr. Foundation, p. 97

77. Levy, D. M. (1937) Primary affect hunger. *Amer. J. Psychiat.*, **94**, 643

78. Lewis, H. (1954) *Deprived children (the Mershal experiment). A social and clinical study*, London, Oxford University Press

79. Lorenz, K. Z. (1937) The companion in the bird's world. *Auk*, **54**, 245

80. Lorenz, K. Z. (1950) *The comparative method in studying innate behaviour patterns*. In: Danielli, J. F. & Brown, R., ed., *Physiological mechanisms in animal behaviour*, London, Cambridge University Press (*Symp. Soc. exp. Biol.*, No. 4), p. 221

81. Lowrey, L. G. (1940) Personality distortion and early infant care. *Amer. J. Orthopsychiat.*, **10**, 576

82. McNemar, Q. (1940) A critical examination of the University of Iowa studies of environmental influences upon the IQ. *Psychol. Bull.*, **37**, 63

83. Murphy, G. (1947) *Personality: a biosocial approach to origins and structure*, New York, Harper, p. 903

84. Naess, S. (1959) Mother-child separation and delinquency. *Brit. J. Delinq.*, **10**, 22

85. Pease, D. & Gardner, D. B. (1958) Research on the effects of noncontinuous mothering. *Child Develpm.*, **29**, 141

86. Pinneau, S. R. (1955) The infantile disorders of hospitalism and anaclitic depression. *Psychol. Bull.*, **52**, 429

87. Pringle, M. L. Kellmer & Bossio, V. (1958) A study of deprived children. *Vita humana*, **1**, 65

88. Pringle, M. L. Kellmer & Bossio, V. (1960) Early, prolonged separation and emotional maladjustment. *J. Child Psychol. Psychiat.*, **1**, 37

89. Prugh, D. G., Staub, E. M., Sands, H. H., Kirschbaum, R. M. & Lenihan, E. A. (1953) A study of the emotional reactions of children and families to hospitalization and illness. *Amer. J. Orthopsychiat.*, **23**, 70

90. Rabin, A. I. (1957) Personal maturity of kibbutz (Israeli collective settlement) and non-kibbutz children as reflected in Rorschach findings. *J. project Techn.*, **21**, 148

91. Rabin, A. I. (1958) Infants and children under conditions of " intermittent " mothering in the kibbutz. *Amer. J. Orthopsychiat.*, **28**, 577

92. Rabin, A. I. (1959) Attitudes of kibbutz children to family and parents. *Amer. J. Orthopsychiat.*, **29**, 172

93. Rheingold, H. L. (1956) The modification of social responsiveness in institutional babies. *Monogr. Soc. Res. Child Develpm. Inc.*, **21**, No. 63

94. Rheingold, H. L. & Bayley, N. (1959) The later effects of an experimental modification of mothering. *Child Develpm.*, **30**, 363

95. Robertson, J. (1952) *A two-year-old goes to hospital* (Film: 16 mm.; 45 min.; sound. Distributors: Tavistock Child Development Research Unit, London; New York University Film Library; United Nations, Geneva)

96. Robertson, J. (1953) Some responses of young children to the loss of maternal care. *Nurs. Times*, **49**, 382

97. Robertson, J. (1958) *Young children in hospital*, London, Tavistock Publications

98. Robertson, J. (1958) *Going to hospital with mother* (Film: 16 mm.; 40 min.; sound. Distributors: Tavistock Child Development Research Unit, London; New York University Film Library; United Nations, Geneva)

99. Robertson, J. & Bowlby, J. (1952) Responses of young children to separation from their mothers. *Courrier*, **2**, No. 3, 131

100. Robertson, Joyce (1962) *Mothering as an influence on early development*. In: *Psychoanalytic study of the child*, New York, International Universities Press, Vol. 17 (in press)

101. Rosenbluth, D., Bowlby, J. & Roudinesco, J. (1951) Separation from the mother as a traumatic experience for the child: some notes on obtaining a relevant history. *Courrier*, **1**, No. 11, 9

102. Roudinesco, J. & Appell, G. (1950) Les répercussions de la stabilization hospitalière sur le développement psycho-moteur de jeunes enfants. *Sem. Hôp. Paris*, **26**, 2271

103. Roudinesco, J. & Appell, G. (1951) De certaines répercussions de la carence de soins maternels et de la vie en collectivité sur les enfants de 1 à 4 ans. *Bull. Soc. Méd. Paris*, **67**, 106

104. Rowntree, G. (1955) Early childhood in broken families. *Populat. Stud.*, **8**, 247

105. Schaffer, H. R. (1958) Objective observations of personality development in early infancy. *Brit. J. med. Psychol.*, **31**, 174

106. Schaffer, H. R. & Callender, W. M. (1959) Psychological effects of hospitalization in infancy. *Pediatrics*, **24**, 528

107. Schur, M. (1960) *Discussion of Dr John Bowlby's paper*. In: *Psychoanalytic study of the child*, New York, International Universities Press, Vol. 15, p. 63

108. Siegel, A. E., ed. (1961) *Research issues related to the effects of maternal employment on children*, University Park, Pa., Social Science Research Center of the Pennsylvania State University

109. Skeels, H. M. & Dye, H. B. (1939) A study of the effects of differential stimulation on mentally retarded children. *Proc. & Addr. Amer. Ass. ment. Defec.*, **44**, 114

110. Skeels, H. M. & Fillmore, E. A. (1937) The mental development of children from underprivileged homes. *J. genet. Psychol.*, **50**, 427

111. Skeels, H. M. & Harms, I. (1948) Children with inferior social histories: their mental development in adoptive homes. *J. genet. Psychol.*, **72**, 283

112. Skeels, H. M., Updegraff, R., Wellman, B. & Williams, H. M. (1938) A study of environmental stimulation: an orphanage preschool project. *Iowa Stud. Child Welf.*, **15**, No. 4

113. Skodak, M. & Skeels, H. M. (1949) A final follow-up study of one hundred adopted children. *J. genet. Psychol.*, **75**, 85

114. Spiro, M. E. (1955) Education in a communal village in Israel. *Amer. J. Orthopsychiat.*, **25**, 283

115. Spitz, R. A. (1945) *Hospitalism*. In: *Psychoanalytic study of the child*, New York, International Universities Press, Vol. 1, p. 53

116. Spitz, R. A. (1946) *Hospitalism: a follow-up report*. In: *Psychoanalytic study of the child*, New York, International Universities Press, Vol. 2, p. 113

117. Spitz, R. A. (1949) The role of ecological factors in emotional development in infancy. *Child Develpm.*, **20**, 145

118. Spitz, R. A. (1960) *Discussion of Dr Bowlby's paper*. In: *Psychoanalytic study of the child*, New York, International Universities Press, Vol. 15, p. 85

119. Spitz, R. A. & Wolf, K. M. (1946) *Anaclitic depression*. In: *Psychoanalytic study of the child*, New York, International Universities Press, Vol. 2, p. 313

120. Stolz, L. M. (1960) Effects of maternal employment on children: evidence from research. *Child Develpm.*, **31**, 749

121. Stott, D. H. (1956) The effects of separation from the mother in early life. *Lancet*, **1**, 624

122. Thorpe, W. H. (1950) *The concepts of learning and their relation to those of instinct*. In: Danielli, J. F. & Brown, R., ed., *Physiological mechanisms in animal behaviour*, London, Cambridge University Press (*Symp. Soc. exp. Biol.*, No. 4), p. 387

123. Trasler, G. (1960) *In place of parents*, London, Routledge & Kegan Paul

124. Wardle, C. J. (1961) Two generations of broken homes in the genesis of conduct and behaviour disorders in childhood. *Brit. med. J.*, **2**, 349

125. Wheeler, W. M. (1956) Psychodiagnostic assessments of a child after prolonged separation in early childhood. II. *Brit. J. med. Psychol.*, **29**, 248

126. Williams, J. M. (1961) Children who break down in foster homes: a psychological study of patterns of personality growth in grossly deprived children. *J. Child Psychol. Psychiat.*, **2**, 5

127. Wootton, B. (1959) *Social science and social pathology*, London, Allen & Unwin

128. Yarrow, L. J. (1961) Maternal deprivation: toward an empirical and conceptual re-evaluation. *Psychol. Bull.*, **58**, 459

PUBLIC HEALTH PAPERS

No.		s. d.	$	Sw. fr.
1.	PSYCHIATRIC SERVICES AND ARCHITECTURE. *A. Baker, R. Llewelyn Davies & P. Sivadon* (1959) (59 pages)	3/6	0.60	2.—
2.	EPIDEMIOLOGICAL METHODS IN THE STUDY OF MENTAL DISORDERS. *D. D. Reid* (1960) (79 pages) .	5/–	1.00	3.—
3.	HEALTH SERVICES IN THE USSR. Report Prepared by the Participants in a Study Tour Organized by the World Health Organization (1960) (58 pages)	3/6	0.60	2.—
4.	ASPECTS OF PUBLIC HEALTH NURSING. *Various authors* (1961) (185 pages)	8/6	1.75	5.—
5.	TRENDS IN JUVENILE DELINQUENCY. *T. C. N. Gibbens* (1961) (56 pages)	3/6	0.60	2.—
6.	IONIZING RADIATION AND HEALTH. *Bo Lindell & R. Lowry Dobson* (1961) (81 pages)	5/–	1.00	3.—
7.	BASIC NURSING EDUCATION PROGRAMMES. A GUIDE TO THEIR PLANNING. *Katharine Lyman* (1961) (81 pages)	5/–	1.00	3.—
8.	THE ROLE OF IMMUNIZATION IN COMMUNICABLE DISEASE CONTROL. *Various authors* (1961) (118 pages)	6/8	1.25	4.—
9.	TEACHING OF PSYCHIATRY AND MENTAL HEALTH. *Various authors* (1961) (186 pages)	10/–	2.00	6.—
10.	CONTROL OF SOIL-TRANSMITTED HELMINTHS. *Paul C. Beaver* (1961) (44 pages).	3/6	0.60	2.—
11.	MATERNAL AND CHILD HEALTH IN THE USSR. Report Prepared by the Participants in a Study Tour Organized by the World Health Organization	*In preparation*		
12.	ROAD TRAFFIC ACCIDENTS. Epidemiology, Control and Prevention. *L. G. Norman* (1962) (110 pages) . .	6/8	1.25	4.—
13.	ASPECTS OF WATER POLLUTION CONTROL. *Various authors* (1962) (116 pages)	6/8	1.25	4.—
14.	DEPRIVATION OF MATERNAL CARE. A Reassessment of its Effects. *Various authors* (1962) (165 pages)	10/–	2.00	6.—